HOME
PLUMBING

Contents

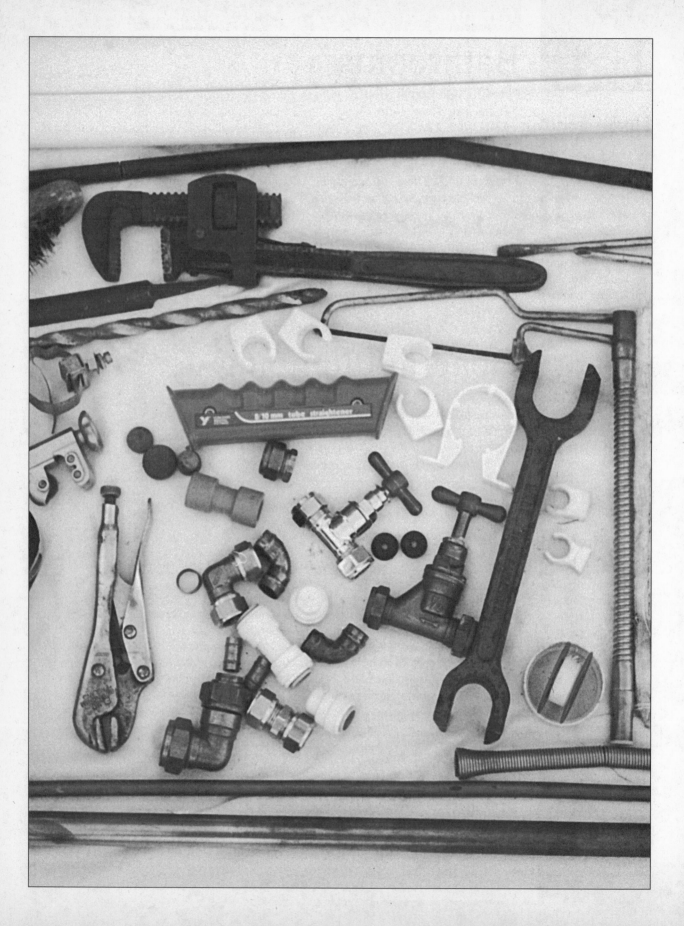

Introduction

Understanding the subject

This book is intended to help you understand the workings of modern water, waste and sanitation systems installed in the home. It covers all aspects of domestic plumbing, from the cold supply entering the property to the soil and waste entering the drains, and describes the alternative systems available, giving their relative performance capabilities.

It also offers practical advice through step-by-step illustrations that show the installation, maintenance and repair of the various plumbing systems and their component parts. The tools and materials needed for plumbing jobs around the home are covered, as are the techniques for using them. Also described are installation and replacement projects for the kitchen and bathroom, methods for dealing with emergencies, and techniques for routine maintenance. The text is written in a clear and concise manner to make the subject easily understood.

Encouraging move

The growth of the DIY superstore, with its large displays of fittings, pipes, tools, etc, has encouraged many competent amateurs to carry out home plumbing work. The modern packaging of parts for specific jobs – such as replacing the waste system on a sink, or installing one for a washing machine – makes the selection of those parts simple. However, because such stores restrict themselves to the faster moving lines, the products displayed are only the tip of the plumbing iceberg.

Indeed, such is the pace of development in domestic plumbing and heating, and because gas work is strictly regulated, that only the plumbers' merchant has the capability and knowledge to stock and sell the wider ranges of product available. Increasingly, you will find that plumbers' merchants have large showrooms and staff trained to answer consumers' questions, and to advise on the suitability of various product types for particular applications. Their wealth of experience can be invaluable when contemplating any form of plumbing work.

Comprehensive coverage

The six chapters of this book fall into two distinct areas: theory and practice. The first two chapters describe the designs of the various systems, the materials and tools required for plumbing work, and the rules and regulations that must be obeyed when carrying out that work. The remaining four chapters cover the range of plumbing jobs that you may wish to tackle – from basic maintenance and repair work to installation of new facilities in kitchen, bathroom and elsewhere in the home.

Although most of the projects in the book are well within the capability of the competent householder, you must take great care to observe all the legal requirements contained within the Water Byelaws, Building Regulations (administered by the local authority), electrical regulations and gas safety regulations. A brief outline of these regulations is provided. Although much gas work requires the same techniques as plumbing jobs, it is a criminal offence for anyone, other than a qualified registered gas installer (CORGI registered), to install, service, maintain or in any other way work on any gas appliance. It is also an offence not to observe the provisions of the Water Byelaws. So it is essential that you are aware of any regulations that may have a bearing on any job you want to carry out. If you think you may have difficulty in doing the work to the required standard, you should employ a professional, and advice of finding a good plumber is given later in the book.

That said, there is no need to be afraid of tackling a wide range of plumbing jobs, as you will see from the various projects shown. Modern plumbing materials make the work quite straightforward, and provided you apply common sense and care, all should go well. When the job has been completed, you will have the satisfaction of knowing that you have done it all yourself, and saved yourself some money in the process.

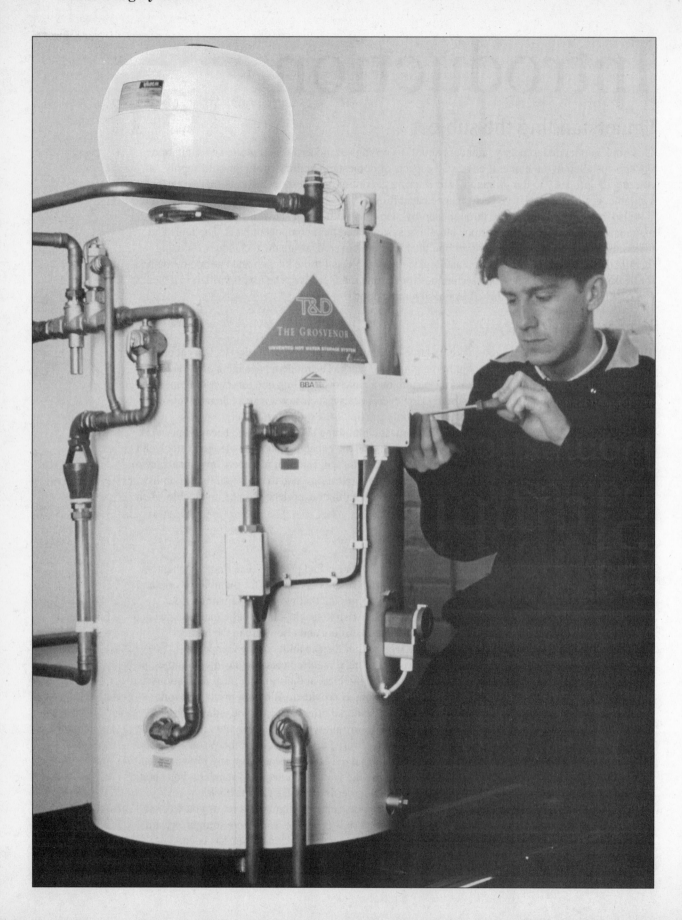

Chapter 1

Plumbing Systems
Domestic supplies

The domestic plumbing system divides neatly into two main parts: the water supply system and the waste/soil system. The supply system transports clean water to the various outlets, cisterns and appliances. The waste and soil system removes contaminated water from sinks, showers, baths, etc, and soil from the lavatories to the underground sewer, septic tank or cesspool, where it can be disposed of safely.

These are two entirely separate systems. Many of the rules and regulations in both the Water Byelaws and the Building Regulations are aimed specifically at ensuring that they remain separate, to avoid contamination of the incoming water supply.

The water system

Most consumers receive their water from the mains network of the local water company, with only a small number having a private supply from a well or borehole. Water in the mains is treated by the water companies so that it is potable, in other words fit for human consumption. Water from wells or boreholes may not necessarily be potable, in which case it will need treatment before use.

By law, the water company must supply potable water to the consumer, but this responsibility stops at the stopvalve at, or near, the boundary of the property. This stopvalve can usually be found under the footpath, below a metal cover.

The pipe from the underground stopvalve to the stoptap inside the property, known as the service pipe, is the responsibility of the owner of the property. This is important for two reasons. If the pipe is of lead, and many still are, it may give rise to lead contamination in the water, and should be replaced. Many water companies are working with consumers to replace lead service pipes, contractors usually tackling a road, or part of a road, at a time. However, the property owner must still pay the cost of replacement, although this will be much lower than would be the case if the job was carried out purely on a one-off basis.

If the pipe develops a leak, the owner must arrange to have it repaired, either by the water company or an independent contractor. If the leak is not repaired as soon as possible, the water company may go ahead and do the work, then send the owner the bill. In extreme cases, the water company may simply turn the water off at their stopvalve until the leak is fixed. After all, it is an offence under the Water Byelaws to waste water, or allow waste to continue.

The service pipe to the property will run underground (at least 75cm/30in deep to protect it from frost), through or under the foundation wall (inside a drainpipe for protection), and terminate at the main stopvalve to the property. This point is the beginning of the internal water supply system.

Materials for service pipes have included lead, galvanised iron and copper, but today it is common practice to use plastic pipe for both new-build and replacement installations. If a metal pipe is replaced by plastic, it is essential to provide a separate ground earth. At one time, the metal pipes of a property were used as the ground earth for the domestic electrical system (see page 60). Nowadays, electrical supply companies provide a separate earthing terminal within the property for the consumer to use.

The mains stopvalve

The mains stopvalve (also termed stoptap or stopcock) is usually located under the kitchen sink. This is because at least one cold tap in the property must be served by water direct from the mains for drinking purposes, and this tap is usually the kitchen cold tap, logically used for food and drink preparation. However, the stopvalve may be found in other places – the bathroom, understairs cupboard, garage or even under floorboards, for example. This last location is not recommended because, in an emergency, the stopvalve must be easily accessible. There may be no internal stopvalve at all in some old properties, in which case the sooner one is fitted the better. This stopvalve is the first line of defence in an emergency, such as a burst pipe, and even if the effect of turning the stopvalve off is not immediate, damage from the limited amount of stored

▶ **SEE PAGE 118 FOR STEP-BY-STEP INSTRUCTIONS ON INSTALLING A NEW STOPVALVE**

water in the house will be far less than if the water was left running at mains pressure.

Not only should the location of the stopvalve be known, but you should also make sure that it can be turned off easily. A stopvalve that is not used can, and probably will, seize up. However, this can be prevented by turning it off (clockwise) and on again every 4-6 months to ensure easy movement. When turning the stopvalve on, never leave it fully open; a quarter-turn off will prevent the mechanism from jamming without affecting the flow.

Immediately above the stopvalve, and usually combined with it, should be a drain valve. This will allow the system to be emptied at what is normally the lowest point. From the stopvalve/drain valve assembly, the rising main delivers water to both the cold and hot water systems of the property.

The cold water system

There are two distinct types of cold water supply system: direct and indirect. The direct type supplies cold water at mains pressure to all outlets in the property. The indirect type provides a direct supply to the kitchen cold tap, and pipes water to a storage cistern, which feeds all the remaining cold and hot water outlets, but at a pressure entirely dependent upon the height of the cistern above each outlet. The storage cistern is usually in the loft, but it may be installed at the highest available point inside the house if, for some reason, the loft is inaccessible. It may also be combined with the hot water cylinder.

Direct supply

In a direct supply system, all cold taps and other outlets, such as WCs, are connected directly to the rising main and operate at mains pressure. Therefore, it is essential to ensure that any float valve replacement is of the correct high-pressure type.

In such a system, the rising main may also continue into the loft, or elsewhere, to supply a cistern that feeds the hot water supply cylinder. In this case, the cold water supply will be at high pressure, and the hot water at low pressure; in other words, unbalanced. This makes the correct selection of mixer units (for showers and the like) vital.

However, alternative methods of supplying hot water are now quite common – the combi boiler, multipoint or mains-pressure storage system, etc. These do not require a high-level cold water cistern.

Water is supplied to your home along a branch pipe from the street mains. The water authority can control the supply by means of a stopvalve near the boundary of your property. From there, the water is carried through the service pipe, under the foundations, and enters the property as the rising main. A stopvalve on the rising main allows you to turn off the supply in an emergency, or for repair work.

Feed and expansion tanks

Alongside any cistern in the loft may be a smaller water tank with pipes connected to the central heating system. This tank will also be supplied with water by the rising main, and through a float valve.

Cisterns

At one time, the cistern, being the only connection to the mains supply except for the kitchen tap, was the main defence against contamination of the mains water supply. This was achieved by feeding the cistern through a float valve, positioned so that there was a constant air gap between the valve outlet and the overflow level.

The float valve operates under the action of a plastic or metal float that rests on the surface of the water. This closes the valve as the water rises towards the maximum level, and opens it when the water level falls. Note that this valve must be a high-pressure version, since it is connected to the mains; a valve in a lavatory cistern, fed from another cistern, must be of a low-pressure type.

Cisterns are also fitted with an overflow pipe, more correctly called a warning pipe, which passes through an

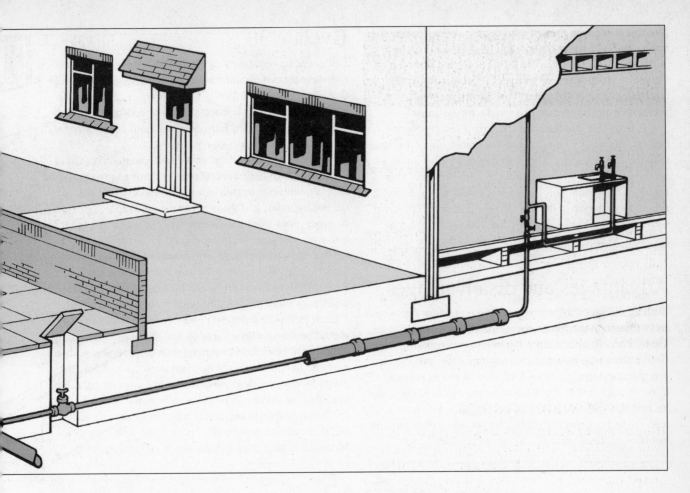

outside wall and ends where any discharge from the pipe can be seen clearly. Any dripping or flow from the pipe clearly indicates that something is wrong, and must be attended to quickly to comply with the byelaws on water wastage. Also, if that warning pipe should become blocked, the water would be pouring into the property and not safely outside.

Being fed by only one pipe, even at mains pressure, but itself feeding a number of outlets all capable of being used at the same time, the cold water cistern must be of an adequate size to provide a reserve of water. The normal recommended size is 227 litres (50 gallons) actual capacity, but larger properties with higher water demand will require a larger capacity. This can be provided by a larger cistern, by joining two cisterns together with two 28mm pipes at low level, or by using one of the new, long, small-section, high-capacity cisterns designed to pass through small loft openings.

▶ **SEE PAGE 128 FOR STEP-BY-STEP INSTRUCTIONS ON INSTALLING A NEW COLD WATER CISTERN**

Indirect supply

With an indirect cold water system, the only outlets at mains pressure are normally in the kitchen and at the cistern. In the kitchen, in addition to the drinking water tap, other connections to the main could include an outside tap, a washing machine, a dishwasher and a water softener, all of which need a minimum pressure to operate. With these appliances, appropriate fittings and valves that comply with the Water Byelaws must be used. Other connections needing mains pressure would include an instantaneous electric shower or gas water heater, but it must be noted that connections to all of these appliances must be made after the connection to the kitchen tap.

For many years, this was the only type of cold water system permitted by most water authorities, as it minimises the possibilities of contamination by physically separating most of the water supply in the property from the mains at the cistern float valve. Nowadays, with the advent of multipoint water heaters, combi boilers and unvented systems, the rules have changed, and other safeguards are required to prevent contamination.

The cold water cistern may be in the loft or roof space, or where this is not available, at as high a point as possible within the property. It acts as a store, feeding the remaining cold water outlets, and the hot water system.

Because both hot and cold supplies are fed from the same cistern, they are at the same, relatively low, pressure and, therefore, are balanced. This allows such outlets as mixer showers to operate in a satisfactory manner.

It is from this that the term UK Low Pressure System derives, the supply being at a considerably lower pressure than the mains supply. This is in contrast to the situation on the Continent, where all pressures are high. For this reason, Continental taps do not work well with the low pressures common in the UK, although they will perform well where modern mains pressure systems have been installed. With the indirect system, the higher the position of the cistern, the better the pressure of water at the taps.

Advantages and disadvantages

With an indirect cold water system, the need for pipework and a cistern in the loft increases the risk of freezing. Modern practice eliminates this by using plumbing systems that take pipe and cisterns out of the loft.

A direct system provides good flow at mains pressure from all cold outlets, but there is no reserve of water if the mains supply is cut off. An indirect system does have that reserve, and is generally quieter. However, it may provide insufficient 'head' of water for an acceptable shower.

Byelaw 30

Under the requirements of Water Byelaw 30, a new or replacement cistern must have a close-fitting lid to ensure that water used for washing and bathing is clean and not contaminated by dust, insects, birds or rodents that might gain access to the loft. However, it should not be airtight, so it must have a mesh-covered air vent.

The cistern will feed either the hot system only (direct cold supply) or both hot and cold systems (indirect cold supply), with one or two exit pipes respectively: one to the hot cylinder, and the other to the cold taps. There may be other pipes from the cistern, feeding water to a bidet or a shower. Separate feeds are necessary to minimise variations in temperature at a shower outlet when another facility (such as a lavatory) is used at the same time. Rising-flow bidets must be fed by separate dedicated pipes to prevent the possibility of cross-contamination.

Each feed pipe from the cistern (normally 22mm) should be fitted with a valve so that the individual water circuits can be isolated for maintenance or repair, without the need to shut down the entire system. In addition, the mains pipe to the float valve must have a servicing valve to enable the cistern to be isolated from the mains.

All valves should be clearly labelled to identify each water circuit. They should be positioned where they can be reached quickly in an emergency and maintained

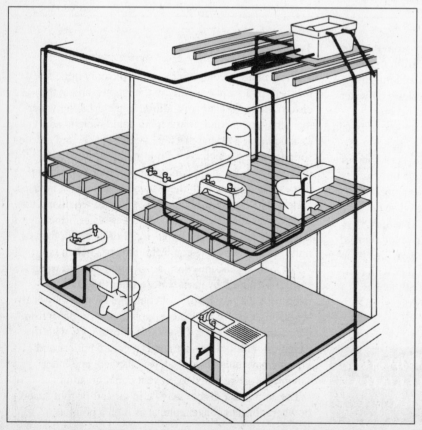

In an indirect cold water supply system, the kitchen tap is fed directly from the rising main. A washing machine or dishwasher may also be linked to the rising main, as will an outside tap. The remainder of the cold outlets in the property are supplied from a storage cistern in the roof, which is fed by the rising main. The cistern supplies water to the hot water cylinder as well.

easily. They should not be hidden behind cylinders in airing cupboards, nor under the cistern in the loft. Often, the best place is in the airing cupboard, at the side of, or above, the cylinder and within easy reach.

Insulation

Another requirement of the Water Byelaws is that every pipe and water fitting, including water cisterns, shall be protected from damage from freezing. Insulation is an effective method of protecting pipes and fittings in vulnerable areas, such as lofts.

However, no insulation of any type can prevent static water in a pipe from ultimately freezing, so if long-term protection in continuous freezing conditions is required, other means of preventing the problem must be used.

By minimising heat loss, insulation can delay the onset of freezing to a greater or lesser extent, depending on the type and thickness of the insulation, and the size of the pipe. Small pipes are more vulnerable than large ones.

Choice of material is important, especially where moisture may be present through condensation, etc. A pipe insulated with dry material may take up to seven hours to freeze, but if the insulation has absorbed moisture, the time could be reduced to less than 30 minutes. Therefore, pipe insulation made from a closed-cell material should be used, such as foamed polyethylene or foamed nitrile synthetic rubber, which have very low water absorption properties.

Wrapping pipe in hair felt or mineral wool is not easy or very efficient. The only effective way is to use formed insulation that is taped in position, with bends accurately cut and taped, so that there are no gaps at any point where heat can escape easily.

For added protection, valves should be lagged at least to the same standard as the pipework and the cistern. Ideally, purpose-designed valve jackets should be used, but it is not difficult to wrap valves thoroughly with felt or glassfibre for effective insulation. The minimum thickness of insulation to meet the byelaws is:

- For 15mm pipe – 25mm (1in)
- For 22-28mm pipe – 19mm (¾in)
- For 35mm pipe and over – 9mm (⅜in)

However, it is recommended that insulation thickness should be equivalent to the pipe outside diameter (OD). For example, 28mm pipe should be lagged with 28mm (1⅛in) wall thickness insulation.

When insulating a cold water cistern in the loft, the top and sides should be well covered. The loft insulation should not extend under the cistern, but be brought up to the sides to provide continuity. Heat from the rooms below will pass through the uninsulated portion of ceiling under the cistern to reinforce the effect of the insulation.

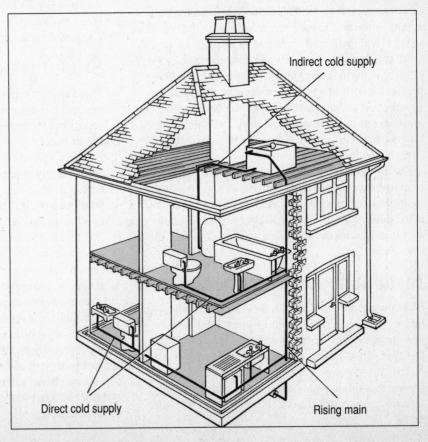

In a direct cold water supply system, all of the cold water outlets in the property are fed directly from the rising main, so all provide good flow at high pressure, and all taps can dispense drinkable water. Depending on the method of providing hot water, there may or may not be a storage cistern in the roof space to supply the hot water cylinder.

Indirect cold supply

Direct cold supply

Rising main

The hot water system

Unlike the cold water system – where there are two basic methods of supply, direct or indirect – the possibilities for the supply of hot water are many and varied. They range from simple gas or electric, single point-of-use heaters for one outlet, to much more complex, centralised boiler systems that supply hot water to a multiplicity of outlets scattered throughout the property. Their locations could include the kitchen, utility room, cloakroom, bathrooms, shower cubicles and any bedrooms provided with water services.

Generally, a hot water system cannot be considered in isolation from the central heating, because most modern systems combine both functions. However, the scope of this book does not extend to central heating systems, which will only be referred to as the source of heat for the domestic hot water supply.

The performance of the system, the water flow rate, water pressure, heat recovery rate, etc, depend on the system design, and can vary quite widely from one system to another.

Thermal expansion

Like most materials, water expands when it is heated. If this expansion is restrained, the pressure can increase significantly, and in the extreme will cause the container to burst with potentially devastating effects.

Also, although water boils and turns to steam at 100°C (212°F) at normal atmospheric pressure, at a higher pressure it boils at a higher temperature. If water, superheated under pressure, bursts its container, the pressure returns to normal, and the water will instantly flash to steam at some 500 times its water volume, exploding with tremendous force.

For this reason, all hot water systems are either vented to atmosphere, or are fitted with expansion vessels and multiple safety devices, as found on unvented systems. With single point-of-use appliances, control is on the cold supply side, with the expansion accommodated in the open spout.

Instantaneous water heaters

Most people are familiar with the Ascot over-sink water heater, which is a single point-of-use water heater serving just the one outlet. There are several modern versions of this type of gas heater, as well as the rather more common electrically-powered units. In fact, the modern electric shower is a single point-of-use water heater, the only difference being that it has a shower head as its outlet instead of a tap. Electric units are available for under-sink mounting in the kitchen, but this type of heater needs a special tap.

The multipoint feeds hot water to a number of outlets on demand. Turn on the tap, the heater fires up or the electricity switches on, water flows, and eventually heated water appears. The amount of time this takes depends on the length of pipe from the unit to the tap. The rate of flow is not very high because the water needs to pass relatively slowly through the heat exchanger to acquire sufficient heat.

The combi boiler is a modern version of the multipoint, but with an added central heating function. Flow rates with this type of appliance are limited, and generally not as good as those of other systems. However, the latest combi boilers have much improved flow rates compared to older versions.

With any of these appliances, no water storage cistern is required, because all are fed directly from the cold water supply. As a result, there is no reserve for washing, etc, in the event of a mains failure. However, the possibility of an interruption to the mains water supply is fairly remote, and inconvenience usually minimal. Whenever major water works are to be undertaken, consumers are normally warned well in advance so that they can take appropriate measures.

Stored water systems

There are two types of stored water system: vented and unvented. Within these two types, there are several variations. However, all of them are based on a cylinder full of water.

With a vented system, when the water is heated and consequently expands, the expansion is taken up in the feed and expansion pipework to the cold water cistern and the cistern itself. The pipework is open to the atmosphere; in other words, vented.

With an unvented system, the expansion is accommodated by an expansion vessel, which is not vented to atmosphere. This may be located remotely from, above, or even inside, the cylinder.

In an unvented system, higher pressures are developed than those in a vented system, and a number of safety devices must be fitted to ensure that it operates safely. Also, regulations demand that these systems are of an approved type, and installed only by a qualified person.

In combined central heating and hot water systems, both hot water and central heating may be vented or unvented (sealed).

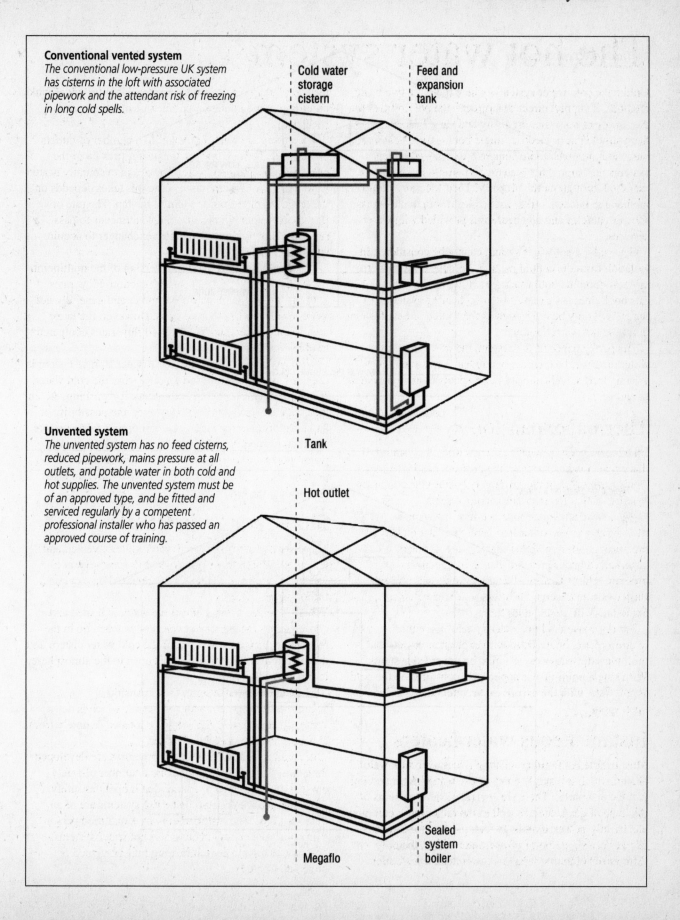

Conventional vented system

The conventional low-pressure UK system has cisterns in the loft with associated pipework and the attendant risk of freezing in long cold spells.

Cold water storage cistern

Feed and expansion tank

Tank

Unvented system

The unvented system has no feed cisterns, reduced pipework, mains pressure at all outlets, and potable water in both cold and hot supplies. The unvented system must be of an approved type, and be fitted and serviced regularly by a competent professional installer who has passed an approved course of training.

Hot outlet

Megaflo

Sealed system boiler

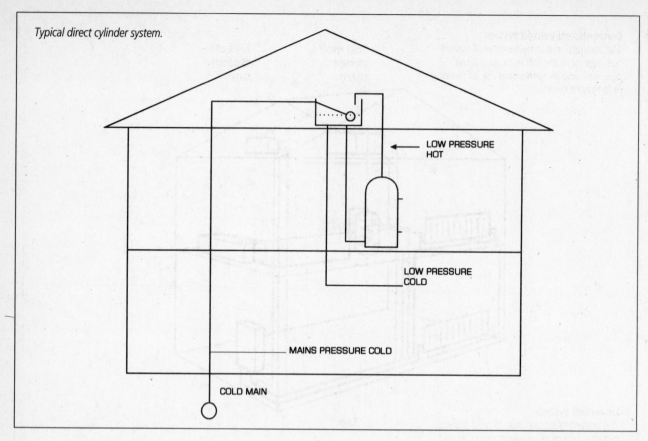

Typical direct cylinder system.

LOW PRESSURE HOT

LOW PRESSURE COLD

MAINS PRESSURE COLD

COLD MAIN

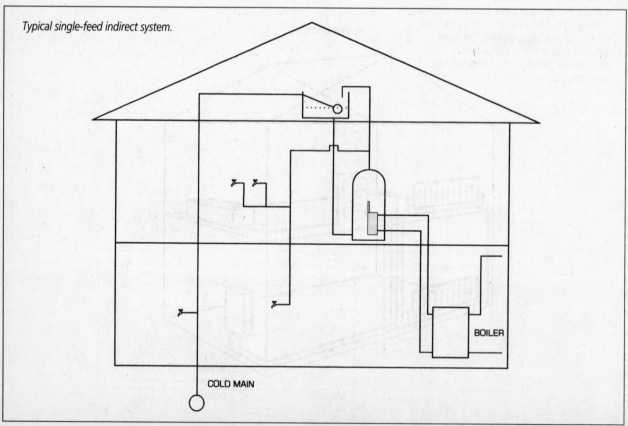

Typical single-feed indirect system.

BOILER

COLD MAIN

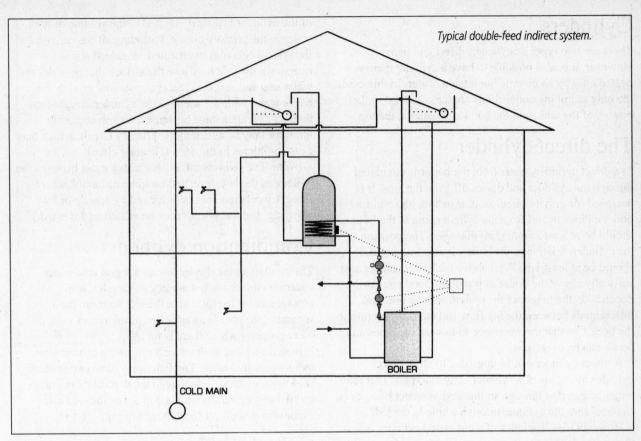

Typical double-feed indirect system.

BOILER

COLD MAIN

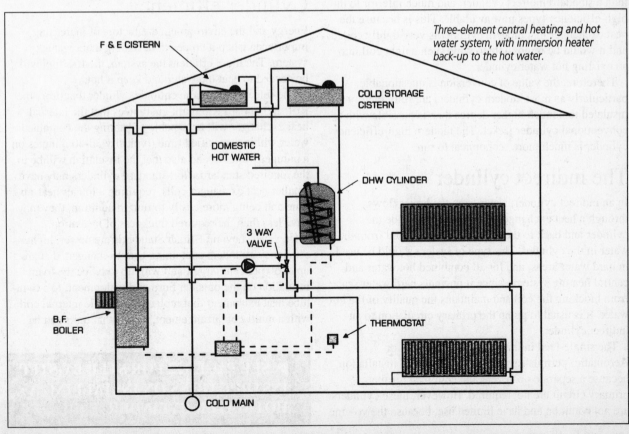

Three-element central heating and hot water system, with immersion heater back-up to the hot water.

F & E CISTERN

COLD STORAGE CISTERN

DOMESTIC HOT WATER

DHW CYLINDER

3 WAY VALVE

B.F. BOILER

THERMOSTAT

COLD MAIN

Cylinders

There are two types of cylinder: direct and indirect. However, it is also possible to have a cylinder that is heated only by an electric immersion heater. In this case, the only plumbing connections are the cold feed to the bottom of the tank, and the hot water outlet at the top.

The direct cylinder

In a direct cylinder, water from the boiler is circulated through the cylinder and drawn off from the taps. It is designed for gravity circulation, usually with solid fuel boilers. Pipes to and from the cylinder, and to the boiler, should be at least 25mm (1in) diameter. The position of the cylinder, relative to the boiler, is also important. It should be at least 1m (39in) above the boiler, and as near vertically above the boiler as possible. Good circulation depends on the height of the system and the pressure differentials between the hot flow and the cooler return to the boiler, so that the resistance to flow of the pipes and bends can be overcome.

A direct cylinder can be upgraded to an indirect cylinder by means of a cylinder conversion kit. This may either be inserted through an immersion heater boss, or be 'wound' into the cylinder through a hole in the side.

However, the efficiency of a converted cylinder is less than a standard indirect cylinder, and much inferior to the high-efficiency types now available. This is because the heat exchanger in a modern cylinder is very tightly coiled, and it would be impossible to wind such a tight coil into an existing hot water cylinder.

Therefore, the value of conversion is questionable, particularly as most modern cylinders are fully factory insulated to a much higher degree than is possible with a conventional cylinder jacket. The modern high-efficiency cylinder is much more economical to run.

The indirect cylinder

In an indirect cylinder, water from the boiler flows through a heat exchanger (usually a coil) inside the cylinder and back to the boiler, being separated from the water in the cylinder. This type of system should be used in hard water areas, and for all combined hot water and central heating systems, since it prevents hard water scale from blocking the coil and maintains the quality of the hot water. It is usual to pump the primary circulation to an indirect cylinder.

The single-feed indirect cylinder (Primatic or Aeromatic) permits savings on materials and installation, because a separate open vent and cold feed for the primary circuit are not required. However, these cylinders are not common and have limited use, because the volume of the cylinder is directly related to the volume of the water in the primary circuit, including all the radiators. If the system becomes overheated, or indeed if it is oversized, the unit may lose the airlock that provides the water seal and revert to direct circulation, mixing the boiler water with the water in the cylinder. Single-feed indirect cylinders must be vented, and no corrosion inhibitor may be added to the primary circuit, which may cause problems in the central heating circuit.

(*Note* The primary circuit circulates water between the boiler and the hot store, and includes radiators, where fitted. Circulation may be achieved by gravity or by pumping, and the system may be vented or unvented.)

Combination cylinders

The combination cylinder has an integral cold water cistern on top of the hot water cylinder. Such an arrangement is useful where there is no room for a separate cold water storage cistern, such as in a flat or other property where there is no loft.

Both direct and indirect versions of the combination cylinder are available. The latter may have two separate cold water cisterns: one to feed the domestic hot water, and the other (usually smaller) to act as the feed and expansion system for the central heating.

Cylinder efficiency

Energy and the environment are factors of increasing importance when it comes to designing a hot water system. The more efficient the system, the less fuel will be needed to heat the water and keep it hot.

The selection of a conventional cylinder that bears the British Standard Kitemark guarantees that the internal heat exchanger will be capable of heating the contained water within a specified time (typically 30-40 minutes on a pumped system), and also that the insulation will be to the required standard. Non-standard cylinders may have smaller heat exchanger coils, requiring a longer heat-up time and being more costly to run. In addition, they may have less than the required thickness of insulation.

However, beyond British Standards are newer, higher-efficiency cylinders containing heat exchangers that are up to 50 per cent larger, and with up to twice the foam insulation on the outside. Further development, to a twin-tube heat exchanger that replaces the single internal coil with a multi-coil arrangement, means that units can be

▶ **SEE PAGE 122 FOR STEP-BY-STEP INSTRUCTIONS ON INSTALLING A HOT WATER CYLINDER**

System A - Recommended

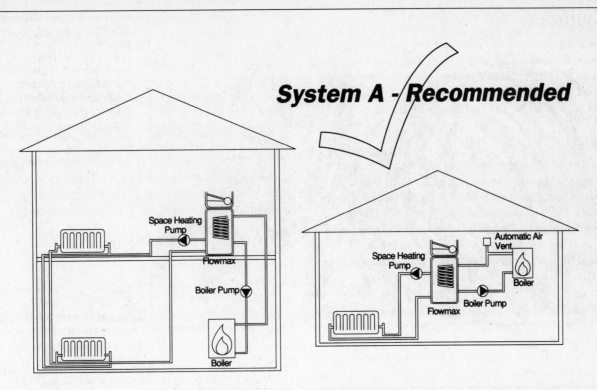

In the storage water mains-pressure system, the boiler heats water directly in a vented store, and the hot water supply, direct from the mains, is heated by passing through a high-efficiency, coil heat exchanger inside the store. The boiler water in the store is also pumped around the central heating system. There is no cistern in the loft, but care must be taken to ensure that the level of water in the store is higher than the top of any radiator. This type of system may be installed by any competent plumber.

System B - Not Recommended

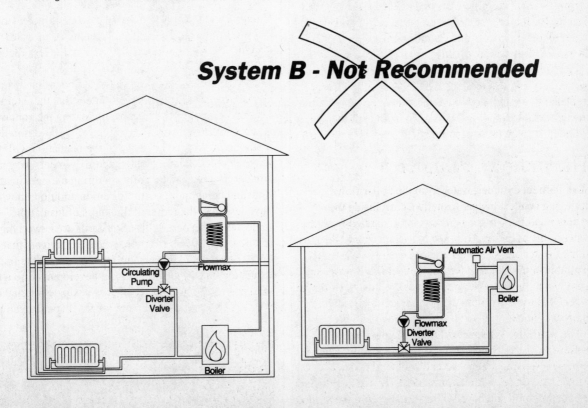

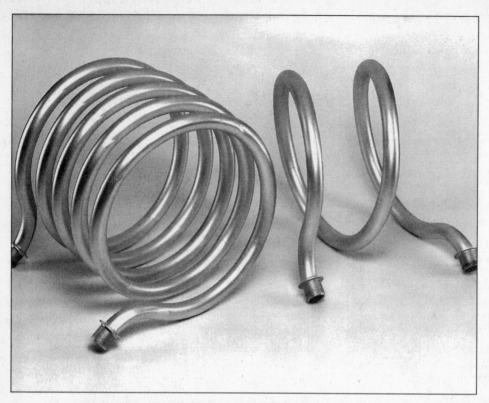

Left *The coil heat exchanger for a British Standard cylinder (left), and a non-standard cylinder coil for converting a direct cylinder to indirect use. The difference in heating capability is very evident. Recent changes to the Building Regulations have made the non-BS unit unacceptable.*

Below *Superduty cylinders may be used to provide higher capacity from the same cylinder size, or to obtain the same performance from a much smaller cylinder than the BS version, freeing airing cupboard space in the process.*

much smaller, more efficient and offer a considerably faster recovery time than even the British Standard cylinder. These units are slightly more expensive than the standard cylinders, but repay the increased cost in greater efficiency (and more space in the airing cupboard).

Pressure

All these types of cylinder are of the low-pressure variety, the pressure and flow of water at the outlets being entirely dependent on the height of the base of the cold water cistern above the outlet. This is known as the 'head' of water. The head is measured to the bottom of the cistern, rather than to the water level, to allow for pressure loss in the pipes, bends and fittings.

Pressure may be measured in lb/sq in, in bar (one atmosphere at about 14.5lb/sq in) or in feet of water (one bar is approximately equivalent to a column of water 30ft/9m high). The bar is the modern unit. Mains water must be delivered to the outer stopcock at a minimum pressure of one bar, but is normally at 2-3 bar. A cold water cistern 10ft (3m) above a tap will provide a pressure of $^{10}\!/_{30}$ bar, in other words a third of a bar – only ten per cent of mains water pressure. This is why taps and other

fittings designed for Continental use do not work well on low-pressure UK systems. However, there are now two ways by which the outlet pressure may be much nearer mains water pressure. These will give the performance of a power shower, without a pump, or fill a bath at twice the rate of other systems. One method is the vented mains-pressure thermal store, and the other the unvented system.

The thermal store

In the thermal store, the safety and simplicity of the traditional UK system is combined with the much higher hot water performance available from utilising the pressure of the water mains. As the name implies, the system stores hot water from the boiler, which is utilised to heat the hot water indirectly, and directly heat any radiators in the central heating system.

The thermal store operates in the reverse manner to the conventional indirect cylinder. With the latter, secondary water is stored in the cylinder for draw-off as required, and it is heated by primary water from a boiler passing through a heat exchanger (coil) inside the cylinder. In a thermal storage system, all the water contained in the unit is primary water, supplied directly from the boiler at

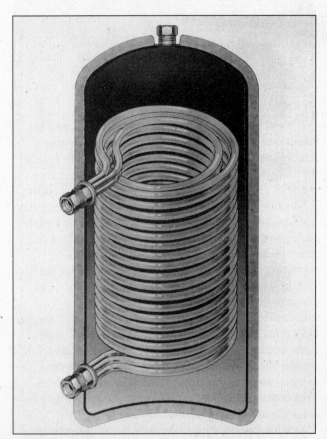

Modern designs of coil are very efficient. This Superduty model, from Albion, has multiple coils for much improved output.

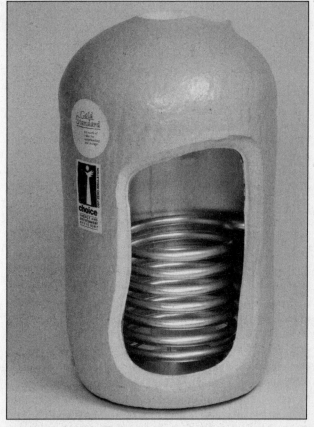

A cutaway of a high-efficiency, indirect cylinder, showing the coil and factory-fitted foam insulation.

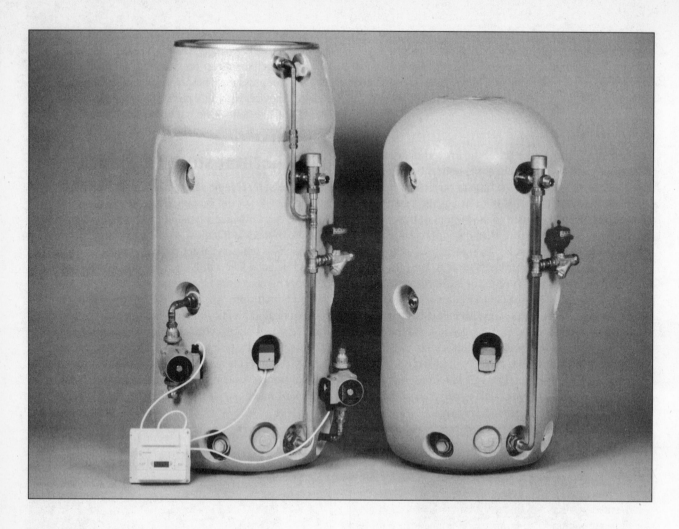

operating temperature, so that the design store temperature is quickly attained.

Water from the tap is heated as required by passing it through a high-efficiency heat exchanger in the thermal store. As the store operates at a higher temperature (75°C/168°F) than is normal with a conventional cylinder (60-65°C/140-150°F), to provide optimum performance, a thermostatic blending valve is usually fitted to restrict draw-off temperature to about 55°C (130°F).

Because the heat exchanger has a capacity of less than 15 litres (3 gallons) and the store itself is vented, the Building Regulations that apply to unvented systems are not applicable. This means that such a system may be installed by any competent person.

Since all outlets are supplied by the mains, balanced pressure between hot and cold water is ensured throughout the dwelling. Flow rates in excess of 20 litres (4½ gallons) per minute mean that a bath and shower can be serviced at the same time, while powerful, invigorating showers are available without the need for a pump (the mains supply to the property must be capable of supporting the level of performance required).

With all outlets at mains pressure, extra care must be taken in sizing of the distribution pipework to ensure a uniform performance throughout the property. In general, the unit will need a 22mm cold supply and 22mm draw-off, with 15mm or smaller pipes run to individual outlets.

Servicing valves can provide a dual function, since they can be used to 'fine tune' flow rates at outlets, as well as taking on their normal role as local isolating valves. In retrofit situations, servicing valves or other flow-restricting devices must be used to prevent part of the system from being starved during conditions of simultaneous draw-off.

Because they incorporate an open vent, thermal storage units offer a wide compatibility with all types of boiler. Even where there is only crude control over combustion, as with a solid-fuel appliance or a wood-burning stove, thermal stores may be used. This is a major difference from unvented systems, where such uncontrolled heating units would be totally unsuitable – and illegal.

As with many other cylinders, the thermal store may also be heated directly by an immersion heater, taking advantage of cheap tariffs when available.

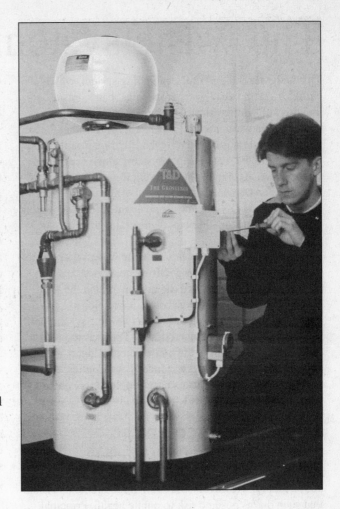

Unvented water heating

With unvented hot water systems, the hot water itself is stored under mains pressure in a vessel fitted with the appropriate safety and functional controls, comprising:

● A thermostat to control hot water temperature.
● An expansion relief valve that will allow the safe release of hot water in the event of failure of the expansion system.
● A combined temperature/pressure relief valve – a mechanical device that opens at a pre-set temperature if the electrical temperature controls fail, or if the pressure builds up abnormally, and a non-self-resetting, high-limit thermostat.

The vessel has no vent to atmosphere, nor a cistern feed, the water being fed directly from the mains.

Water may be heated indirectly by a remote boiler through a primary circuit, which may also supply a central heating circuit. The heat is transferred through a coil in the cylinder to the stored water, as with any indirect cylinder. The water may also be heated directly by immersion heaters or by a gas burner directly heating the surface of the storage vessel (a direct-fired water heater).

Unvented systems fall under the Building Regulations, which require them to be of an approved make and to be fitted by a suitably trained installer, because of the safety implications. If directly gas-fired, they must be fitted, serviced and maintained by a CORGI-registered installer.

Unvented systems may not be used with any boiler not capable of being fully thermostatically controlled, such as a solid-fuel appliance. Nor should they be used with ascending-spray bidets or in any other situation where a Type A air gap should be employed.

It is not advisable to install this type of system where the water pressure is low (3 bar is the recommended mains pressure), where the supply may be intermittent, or where the water contains particles that could block the strainer. Because these units have safety devices that are working parts, they must be regularly serviced and should not be located where there is any possibility of the safety devices being tampered with.

So why, with all these restrictions, should such systems be considered? The answer is simple and unequivocal – performance. No other system can provide the volume of hot water and the high mains pressure that these systems are capable of. The supply pressure and the supply service pipe must be capable of powering this performance. If the service pipe size is less than ¾in (19mm), or the pressure is below 1.5 bar, these systems will not perform to their full potential, although they will still operate safely. The customer should ensure that the installer checks the pressure and flow at a time of maximum local demand, when both will be at their lowest.

These systems are capable of much greater flow than even a mains-pressure thermal storage system. In an unvented system, the water is not slowed by the resistance of the system components – mixing valve, high-efficiency coil, etc – but simply flows under full mains pressure.

In practice, this means that mixer showers provide a better flow; temperature is more stable because of the balanced hot and cold pressures; baths are filled more quickly; and several appliances can be used at once without affecting the individual performance of any. For example, a shower will not be affected by a bath being run, or a WC being flushed.

The other advantage of these units is that they can be located virtually anywhere in the property. The only real restriction is the need to run a pipe from the expansion relief valve so that it can discharge safely to the outside.

The waste system

This is the second part of the plumbing system, which carries away the dirty water from sinks, baths, basins, etc, and the soil from lavatories to the sewer, septic tank or cesspool, via waste and soil pipes. This part of the plumbing system is covered by the Building Regulations, in contrast to the water supply system, which is covered by the Water Byelaws. The Building Regulations are administered by the building control officer of the local authority, to whom you must send details of any proposed major alterations or additions to the drainage system of your property.

In fact, there are three types of waste water: water from washing, soil water discharged from lavatories, and rainwater from the roof and the ground around the property. At one time, it was common practice to keep the waste and soil systems separate in a two-pipe system until they entered the underground drains. This was to prevent 'drain air' from entering the house and causing, it was thought, a variety of illnesses. Indeed, it is highly probable that 'drain air' can cause people to feel unwell, if not actually make them feel physically ill.

Design requirements

Modern practice is to use a single-stack drainage system into which all waste and soil products are discharged above ground. However, strict design requirements ensure that such drains pose no risk to public health. Principal among these requirements is the use of traps, which are fitted to all sanitaryware and contain a water seal to prevent foul air from the drains entering the property. In addition, pipe layout and air admittance valves contribute to safety by ensuring that there is no possibility of the water seal being broken by pressure from within the drainage system.

In an old two-pipe system, the soil pipe is connected directly to the drains at its base, and is open to the air at the top, which should be well above the eaves of the roof. Wastes from baths, basins, etc, will discharge into a hopper head, itself connected to the waste pipe which, in turn, will discharge into an open gully. Waste from kitchen sinks normally discharges into the same gully. Any ground-floor WCs are usually connected directly to the underground drains.

This type of waste system, utilising open hoppers, is considered unsatisfactory, because the hoppers are not self-cleaning and can become blocked with debris. Also, the smell from the pipes may enter the bathroom if the window is open. Although this pipe arrangement was superceded by the single-stack system over 30 years ago, many properties are still fitted with the two-pipe system.

With the modern system, there is only one soil pipe – commonly called the soil stack or discharge pipe – to which all wastes are connected. As with the soil pipe of the two-pipe system, this stack terminates above the eaves and is open to atmosphere, unless a relief valve is fitted to the top of the pipe. Current practice is to install the soil pipe inside the house, rather than on the outside, as used to be the case.

Downstairs wastes may be connected to the soil stack or, if this is not convenient, may be taken out to a gully, as in the older system. However, the Building Regulations demand that the discharge from such a waste is below the level of the gully grid, which means using a back inlet gully, or cutting a hole in the grid for the pipe to pass through. Soil pipes from ground-floor lavatories may be connected to the main soil stack or, again, directly to the underground drains.

Single-stack systems use far less pipework than two-pipe systems and, by being built inside the property, are much less obtrusive. However, they do need careful design and installation to work correctly. There are strict rules governing the size and type of fittings that may be used, and where and how connections can be made to the stack. The design is made much simpler, of course, where all of the sanitary fittings are installed close to the vertical run of the pipe.

Waste pipe and fittings

There are two sizes of waste pipe and fittings: 32mm (1¼in) and 40mm (1½in) diameter. The smaller size is used for washbasins, and the larger size for all other sanitary appliances, including sinks, washing machines, baths, showers, etc.

You may only use the smaller size to run into the larger size, not the other way round. For example, you may run the waste from a washbasin (using 32mm pipe) into the waste system from a bath (using 40mm pipe), but you may not run 40mm pipe into 32mm pipe.

There are three types of plastic waste systems in current use: universal or multifit types employing compression joints; push-fit, which have a simple rubber jointing system; and solvent-weld, where the joints are stuck together with adhesive.

Most plastic waste systems are based on either uPVC or polypropylene piping. Polypropylene pipe must be assembled with universal or push-fit joints, but a uPVC system may also be solvent-welded.

Both types of pipe are installed in the same way.

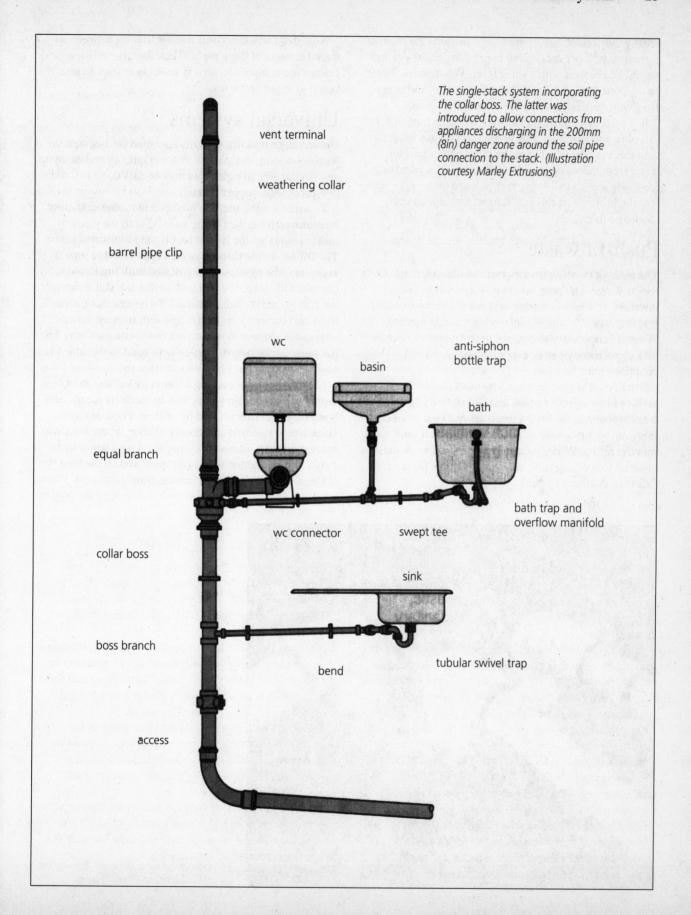

vent terminal

weathering collar

barrel pipe clip

wc

basin

anti-siphon
bottle trap

bath

equal branch

collar boss

wc connector

swept tee

bath trap and
overflow manifold

sink

boss branch

bend

tubular swivel trap

access

The single-stack system incorporating the collar boss. The latter was introduced to allow connections from appliances discharging in the 200mm (8in) danger zone around the soil pipe connection to the stack. (Illustration courtesy Marley Extrusions)

Ideally, horizontal runs should slope towards the drain at a gradient of 2 per cent – 2cm in 1m (¾in in 3ft) – which should be checked with a spirit level. Waste pipes should be supported every 0.5m (20in) horizontally, and every 1m (39in) vertically, using the correct size of clip.

It is preferable to limit pipe runs in 32mm pipe to 1.7m (5ft 6in), and in 40mm pipe to 3m (10ft). Runs longer than this may cause noise in the pipes and/or pull the water from the waste traps by self-siphonage, removing the water seal and allowing free passage of drain air back into the property. If this is a danger, anti-siphon traps should be used.

Push-fit waste

The push-fit system provides fast installation, particularly for polypropylene pipe, where new systems are being installed, or where complete systems are being replaced. It makes use of a simple rubber ring jointing method. When it is necessary to connect push-fit pipes to existing uPVC, polypropylene or copper piping, universal couplings must be used.

Installation is simple. First, you must ensure that the ends of pipes are cut square, and that the cut edges are free from burrs. To make a joint, apply a coat of silicone lubricant to the outside of the pipe and push it fully home into the fitting. Where expansion of the pipework must be allowed for on long runs, withdraw the pipe from the fitting by 5-10mm (¼-⅜in).

Note that there is not full standardisation between all manufacturers of these pipes. Therefore, not all pipes and fittings are compatible, so it is sensible to stick to one brand to avoid problems.

Universal systems

Universal, or multifit, systems are based on a compression jointing system, designed to connect quickly and easily to any similar size of pipe. This may be uPVC, polypropylene, copper or lead.

To make a joint, the nut, washer and rubber seal must be removed from the fitting, and slid onto the pipe, making sure that the rubber seal is the right way round. The fitting should then be pushed fully onto the pipe. If necessary, the pipe can be lubricated with liquid soap. To complete the joint, the seal and washer are slid down to the fitting, and the nut tightened. To ensure that the nut is tightened correctly, tighten it by hand, then use an adjustable spanner to tighten it a further quarter turn. The nut must not be over-tightened with hand tools, which is easily done, as this is likely to damage the seal.

Connection to an existing 110mm uPVC soil stack, for either 40mm or 32mm sizes, can be made by means of a strap-on boss. This is fitted by drilling a hole in the soil stack where required and simply glueing on the boss with solvent cement, which will provide a long-lasting seal. Any such connection to the soil stack must be at least 200mm (8in) from any WC connection.

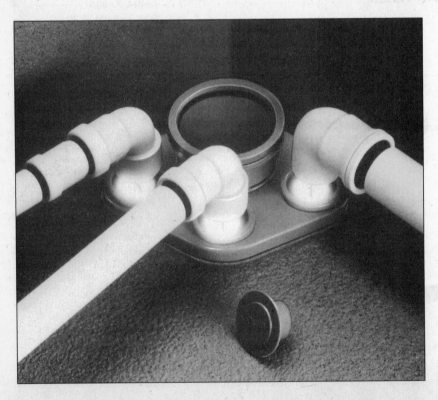

An example of the collar boss, showing the push-fit connection of waste pipes.

Typical domestic sanitary pipework arrangement, incorporating an air admittance 'Durgo' valve. (Illustration courtesy Marley Extrusions)

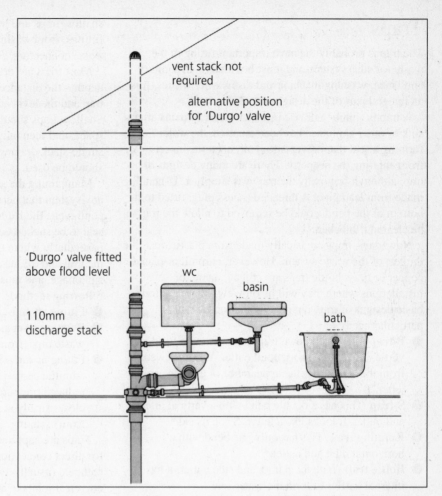

vent stack not required

alternative position for 'Durgo' valve

'Durgo' valve fitted above flood level

110mm discharge stack

wc

basin

bath

Below *The anti-siphon trap.*
A *The normal water seal position.*
B *When the trap is subject to suction, water is pulled out until air begins to be drawn through the central by-pass to break the siphonic action.*
C *The remaining water effectively seals the trap. No foul water is retained in the trap for longer than one flushing operation, as the contents are completely washed through during each discharge.*
(Illustration courtesy Marley Extrusions)

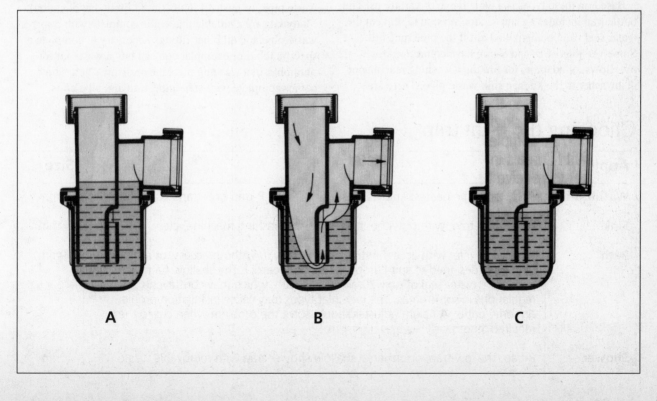

A   B   C

Traps

The trap is probably the most important fitting in the waste (or soil) system, and must be fitted to all sanitary appliance, washing machine and dishwasher wastes. It is an integral part of the design of a WC.

A trap is simply a device in which water remains after a sink or other appliance has been emptied, the water forming a seal that prevents foul air, bacteria, insects, etc, from entering the property. There are many designs of trap, although originally the trap was simply a 'U-bend' made from lead pipe. A threaded access plug, fitted to the bottom of the bend, could be removed to allow the trap to be cleared if blocked.

Nowadays, traps are usually made from plastic, just like the rest of the waste system. However, chromium-plated copper or brass bottle traps are still available for installations where they will be on view. There are four basic designs of trap, but many variations to suit particular needs:

● **P-trap** The best known trap. It has a single bend, a vertical inlet and a horizontal outlet. When viewed from the side, it has the appearance of a crude capital letter 'P'.
● **S-trap** This has a double bend with a vertical inlet and outlet. It looks like a letter 'S' on its side.
● **Running trap** This has only one bend with a horizontal inlet and outlet.
● **Bottle trap** With a top inlet and side outlet, it has internal baffles to form the water seal.

Based on these types is a wide range of variations. The bottle trap includes an anti-siphon version to prevent the water seal from being pulled out if the pipe runs full. Some versions of P- and S-trap have connectors for overflows, or adaptors for linking a washing machine or dishwasher to the kitchen sink waste pipe. There are shallow traps and trap extensions, and a range of other fittings, from washing machine standpipes to flexible waste connectors.

Most traps are designed to provide a 75mm (3in) seal depth – the distance between the normal water level in the trap and the level at which air can pass through it. Shallow traps should only be used where there is limited space, and then only on two-pipe soil systems. With single-stack drainage systems, only the deep-seal trap should be used.

Maintaining the seal in the trap is most important, as any system that permits the seal to be destroyed would contravene the Building Regulations. It is possible for the seal to be sucked out of the trap if the pipe runs full, particularly where there is a long vertical drop between the trap and the stack. This is referred to as self-siphonage, and must be prevented by adopting one of the following methods:
● Fitting an anti-siphon trap.
● Running a separate vent pipe to the stack above the waste pipe, from just beyond the trap.
● Fitting an anti-siphon valve (sometimes called an air admittance valve) to the waste pipe. This opens under reduced pressure in the waste pipe to allow air in, but closes firmly at normal pressure to prevent odours from escaping.

Traps are supplied with screw fittings that are designed for direct connection to the waste outlet of the sink, basin, bath, etc (usually 1¼ or 1½in BSP thread), and either universal joints to accept most materials and makes of waste pipe, or push-fit joints (more limited application). Many kits are available that come complete with trap, waste pipe and all other fittings necessary to complete a specific job. For example, you can buy a waste kit for plumbing-in a washing machine or dishwasher, which comes complete with standpipe, trap and pipe clips.

Choosing the right trap

Appliance	Trap	Size
Washbasin	Bottle trap (the neatest and least obtrusive type), P-trap or S-trap.	32mm
Sink	P-trap or S-trap, with or without adaptors for washing machine, etc.	40mm
Bath	P-trap, low inlet with access; P-trap, low level with/without access; or a shallow bath trap (designed to suit European bath standards). The shallow bath trap provides a water seal of only 20mm (⅞in) depth, which may contravene regulations in some areas. The low-inlet types may cause installation problems on some baths. A height adjuster should solve the problem when cut to the required length.	40mm
Shower	P-trap, shallow trap, or universal shallow shower trap with removable waste.	40mm

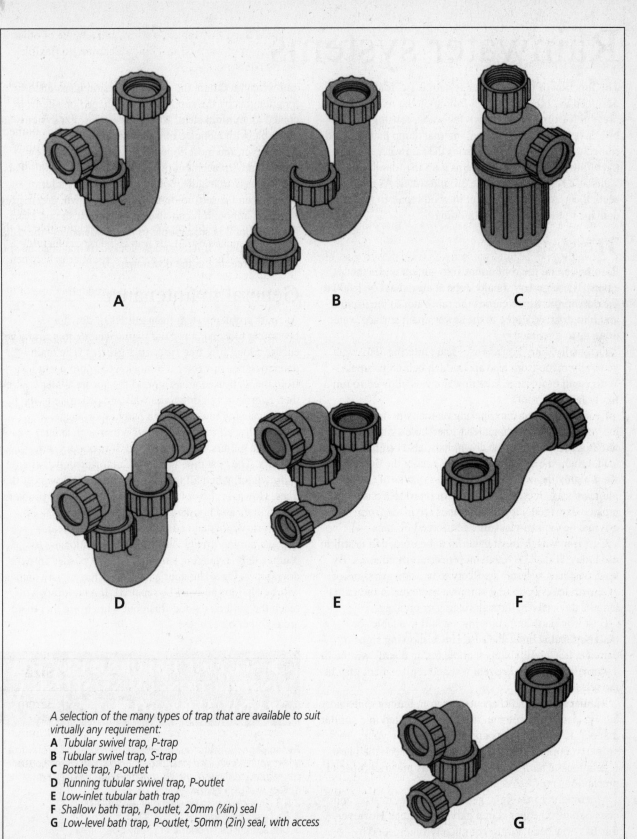

A selection of the many types of trap that are available to suit
virtually any requirement:
A Tubular swivel trap, P-trap
B Tubular swivel trap, S-trap
C Bottle trap, P-outlet
D Running tubular swivel trap, P-outlet
E Low-inlet tubular bath trap
F Shallow bath trap, P-outlet, 20mm (⅞in) seal
G Low-level bath trap, P-outlet, 50mm (2in) seal, with access

Rainwater systems

The function of the rainwater system is twofold. It is designed to collect rainwater falling on the roof area, and prevent it from running down the walls, causing sodden brickwork, water penetration, internal damp patches, and ruined decorations. It also carries the rainwater away from the building to prevent problems with the foundations and walls as a result of excessive ground water. As can be seen, the system must be kept in good repair to prevent damage to the fabric of the building.

The system

Rain falling on the roof drains into gutters under the eaves. These gutters should slope at a gradient of 1:600 to the downpipe, which carries the rainwater to the ground and into drains running to the sewer, main surface water drain or to a soakaway.

Originally, only large houses had guttering. This was generally made from lead and hidden behind parapets. With small properties, the rainwater was allowed to run freely from the roof.

Lead is still used for guttering on many period homes, the water running through lead-lined holes in the parapets, into hoppers and then the downpipes, also originally of lead. Often, the hoppers, and occasionally the downpipes, were highly decorated and remain examples of the plumber's art. Incidentally, modern reproductions to replace damaged hoppers and pipes are made from original designs in glassfibre-reinforced plastics.

Cast iron was the next material to be used, and is still in use today; it may be found on properties of all sizes. By now, cast iron systems are likely to be showing signs of age, with leaks occurring at joints, and even in the gutter lengths themselves, through rusting or breakage.

Cast iron parts and guttering are still available for making repairs, but if the cast iron is showing signs of damage, it is highly likely that the fascia boards will be in a worse state. Complete removal and replacement may be the wisest course.

Similar in size and shape to cast iron, but not quite as heavy, is asbestos cement. It is also connected in a similar manner. If you think this material may be on your property, contact your local authority to check the latest regulations regarding working with this material. Special precautions may be required.

Much lighter in weight, generally smaller in size, and considerably cheaper is thin galvanised steel. However, this has now been almost completely superceded by modern plastic systems.

Similarly, aluminium systems are available, both cast and wrought. Often, the wrought version is installed in long lengths by the supplier, being shaped on site from coated aluminium strip. Aluminium rainwater systems are available with a choice of colour coatings.

However, the most common material for both new houses and replacement of other materials is uPVC. This is light, easy to handle, comes in a range of gutter sections, and is self-coloured in black, brown, green, grey or white, although it can also be painted. It should last a lifetime, but it is susceptible to impact damage – the usual cause of failure. If it becomes blocked, it may also be split by water freezing in the downpipes.

General maintenance

As most problems stem from gutters or downpipes becoming blocked, a regular maintenance programme will ensure a long life, free from emergencies. The main danger comes in winter if a blockage should occur away from the well-used areas around the house. Water could then overflow, run down the wall and penetrate to the inside, causing internal damp patches, or worse.

Normally, all that is needed is a thorough annual clean out of the gutters, downpipes and, if necessary, any hoppers. The best time to do this, unfortunately, is in the early winter, when all the leaves have been blown off the trees. However, leaves are by no means the only problem with gutters and hoppers. It is quite surprising just how much gritty moss can accumulate, even in a year.

Use a garden trowel and bucket, or plastic bag, to remove debris, making sure that it is not pushed into the downpipes. Once the debris has been cleared, any damage will be obvious and can be repaired. If a hose pipe will reach the gutters, a good flush out will ensure that there are no other blockages.

> ▶ **SEE PAGE 136 FOR STEP-BY-STEP INSTRUCTIONS ON INSTALLING A RAINWATER SYSTEM**

Facing page *Rainwater downpipes may be connected directly to an underground drain, or discharge over a gully. Various methods of connection are shown here. (Illustration courtesy Marley Extrusions)*
1 *Back inlet gully hopper*
2 & 3 *Shoe discharging over grid of existing gully*
4 *Back inlet gully trap*
5 *Disc adaptor and mortar fillet to clay pipe*
6 *Reducer to surface water drain*
7 *Spigot to stoneware or pitchfibre socket*
8 *Spigot to cast iron drain socket*

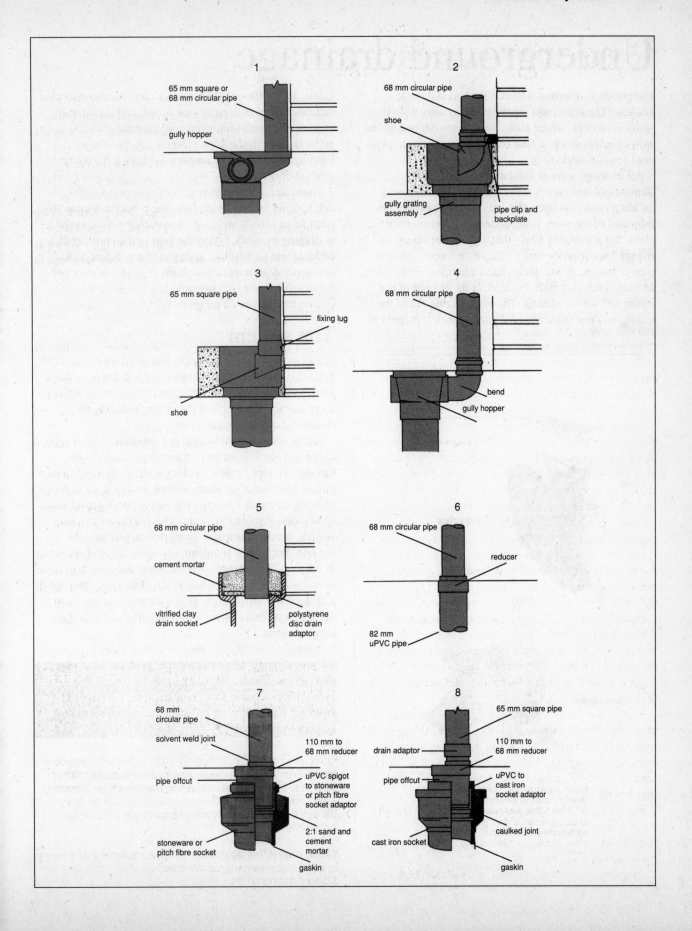

1
65 mm square or 68 mm circular pipe
gully hopper

2
68 mm circular pipe
shoe
gully grating assembly
pipe clip and backplate

3
65 mm square pipe
fixing lug
shoe

4
68 mm circular pipe
bend
gully hopper

5
68 mm circular pipe
cement mortar
vitrified clay drain socket
polystyrene disc drain adaptor

6
68 mm circular pipe
reducer
82 mm uPVC pipe

7
68 mm circular pipe
solvent weld joint
pipe offcut
110 mm to 68 mm reducer
uPVC spigot to stoneware or pitch fibre socket adaptor
stoneware or pitch fibre socket
2:1 sand and cement mortar
gaskin

8
65 mm square pipe
drain adaptor
pipe offcut
110 mm to 68 mm reducer
uPVC to cast iron socket adaptor
cast iron socket
caulked joint
gaskin

Underground drainage

Underground drainage connects the soil and waste household systems, and the rainwater system, with the sewer system or, where public sewers are not available, with a cesspool, septic tank or packaged treatment plant (a mini sewage works).

All drainage work is regulated by the Building Regulations and comes under the control of the local building control officer. Not only must this officer be informed of the work being undertaken and approve the plans, but it is highly likely that regular inspection will be required at various stages as the job proceeds. Also, the type of trench, in which the drains run, may be specified, as well as the materials required for the bottom of the trench and for backfilling. The material dug out of the trench may not be suitable for putting back if it contains stones above 40mm (1½in) in size. This means that other suitable materials must be purchased, and the unused excavated material removed and disposed of in accordance with the Waste Disposal Regulations. Employing a skip hire company is likely to be the best method of disposal.

The materials for drains are easily handled (uPVC is much easier to work with than clay pipes) and joined by push-fit or solvent welding. However, the work involved in digging trenches, laying the pipe to the correct fall, bedding and backfilling, arranging for pressure testing, and generally complying with the regulations may be better left to the professional unless you are absolutely certain that you can manage it.

The system

Waste from the soil pipe (including solid waste from the WC) flows straight into the underground drains without interruption. This ensures that the flow is sufficient to carry any solid matter into the sewer, reducing the likelihood of a blockage occurring.

Waste water and rainwater, not connected above ground to the soil stack, must enter the underground system through a trapped gully. In older systems, it was common practice to discharge waste water over a grid set in the top of a gully, or into a hopper, but this is no longer allowed.

Any new installation, or modification to an existing system, must lead the discharge pipe below the level of the grid, but it must terminate above the level of the water in the trap. This ensures that the water does not discharge over a grid that has been blocked by leaves or other debris and flood the surrounding area with waste water. Also, the action of water flowing unimpeded into the gully keeps it clean.

A simple modification for an existing gully is to pass the pipe through a hole cut into the grid, but for a new installation, a back inlet gully should be used. This incorporates a waste pipe connection in its design. The pipes from the gully, or soil stack, lead directly to an inspection chamber.

grating and plate

baffle plate

main body

32/40/50 mm waste pipe

boss connector

68mm rainwater pipe solvent welded directly into the larger boss upstand, 32, 40 or 50mm waste connected to the smaller upstand via an appropriate boss connector

Left *The compact gully provides a neat, simple and easily installed solution to the majority of cases where an external gully is required. Exposed external waste or downpipe connections can be provided through the cover plate or grating, as applicable. (Illustrations courtesy Marley Extrusions)*

Facing page *Where the compact gully is not suitable, a wide variety of gully combinations may be assembled. (Illustrations courtesy Marley Extrusions*

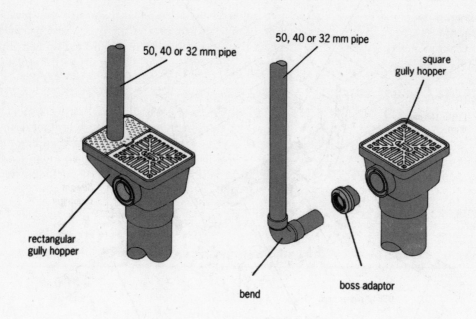

50, 40 or 32 mm pipe

50, 40 or 32 mm pipe

square
gully hopper

rectangular
gully hopper

bend

boss adaptor

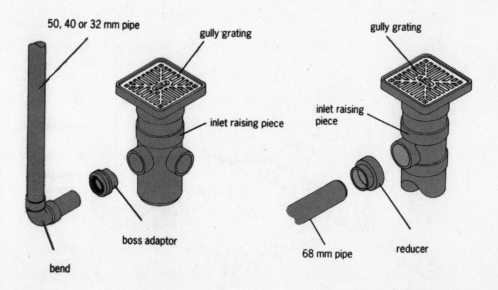

50, 40 or 32 mm pipe

gully grating

gully grating

inlet raising piece

inlet raising
piece

boss adaptor

bend

68 mm pipe

reducer

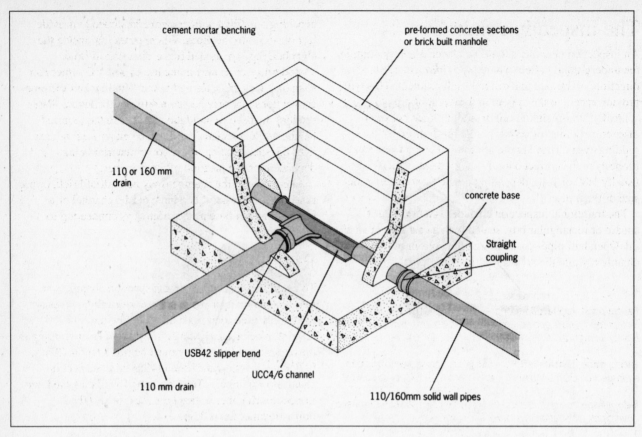

cement mortar benching

pre-formed concrete sections
or brick built manhole

110 or 160 mm
drain

concrete base

Straight
coupling

USB42 slipper bend

UCC4/6 channel

110 mm drain

110/160mm solid wall pipes

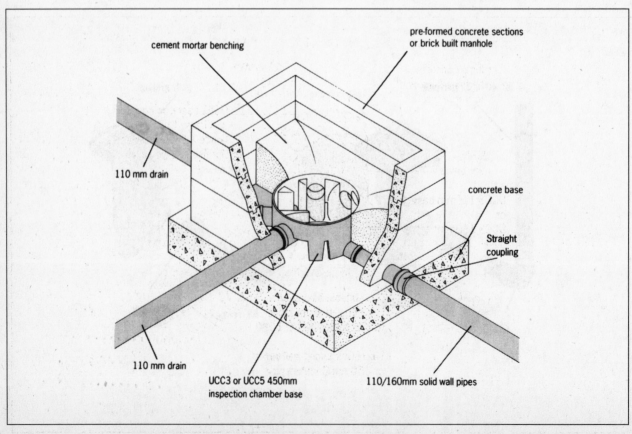

cement mortar benching

pre-formed concrete sections
or brick built manhole

110 mm drain

concrete base

Straight
coupling

110 mm drain

UCC3 or UCC5 450mm
inspection chamber base

110/160mm solid wall pipes

The inspection chamber

An inspection chamber should be placed at every point in the underground system where pipes join, change direction, or are laid to a different fall gradient. This will provide access to the system in the event of a blockage.

Ideally, drains should run in straight lines between inspection points (or access points for drain rods – rodding eyes). They should always fall away from the property at the correct continuous gradient, which is usually 1:80 or 1:40, depending on the flow rate and the size of the pipe.

The traditional inspection chamber is a brick-built square or rectangular box, sealed with a cast iron or steel lid. Open half pipes pass through the bottom of the chamber, while the area surrounding the pipes – the benching – is filled with cement and sloped to provide fast run-off into the pipes. Where pipes join inside the chamber, they are angled in the direction of flow.

Modern systems may make use of a uPVC inspection chamber. This has a formed based with blanked-off pipe connections that may be opened to suit the layout. Riser sections are used to build the chamber to the required height, while a sealed cover may be either steel or cast iron, the specification of the cover material being dependent on the location of the chamber.

Alternatively, the chamber may be built of brick, or pre-cast concrete sections, and have plastic channel or a plastic chamber base as the drainways connecting to plastic pipes.

Rodding eyes

To avoid the need of building inspection chambers at frequent intervals on a single pipe run, rodding eyes are commonly used to provide access to the drains for clearing blockages. However, they only permit rodding in the direction of flow. They must be fitted within 22m (72ft) of a junction and 45m (148ft) of an inspection chamber or manhole. To allow rubbish to be cleared, an inspection chamber or manhole must be installed downstream of the rodding eye.

Facing page, top left *Brick or pre-cast concrete manhole incorporating uPVC open channel components. (Illustration courtesy Marley Extrusions).*

Facing page, bottom left *Brick or concrete manhole incorporating an inspection chamber base. (Illustration courtesy Marley Extrusions)*

Below *Inspection chamber installation, using a plastic base, riser and drain pipes. (Illustration courtesy Marley Extrusions)*

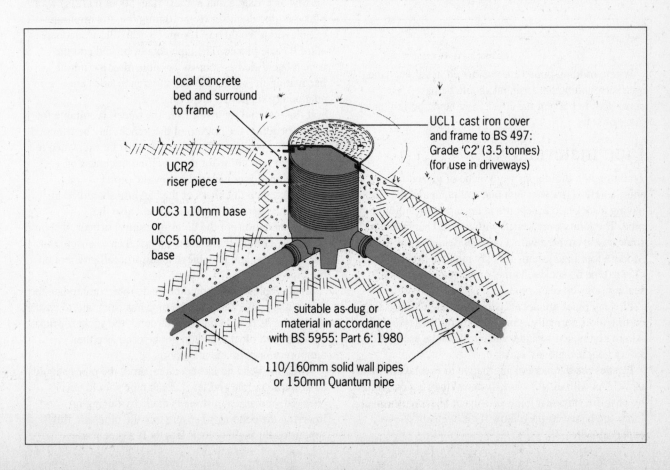

local concrete bed and surround to frame

UCR2 riser piece

UCC3 110mm base
or
UCC5 160mm base

UCL1 cast iron cover and frame to BS 497: Grade 'C2' (3.5 tonnes) (for use in driveways)

suitable as-dug or material in accordance with BS 5955: Part 6: 1980

110/160mm solid wall pipes or 150mm Quantum pipe

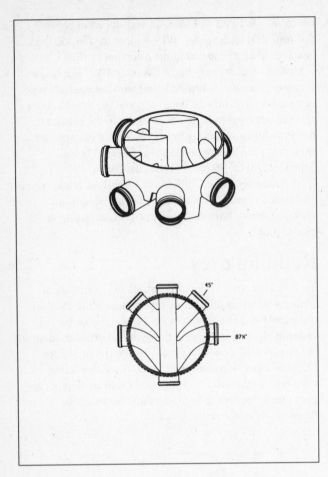

Left *Black polypropylene inspection chamber base with 110mm all-socketed connections, supplied with four blanking plugs. (Illustration courtesy Marley Extrusions)*

Facing page, top *Head of drain rodding point. Rodding points may be located at the head of a drain or in an intermediate position as an alternative to an inspection chamber or manhole. (Illustration courtesy Marley Extrusions)*

Facing page, bottom *Intermediate rodding point. (Illustration courtesy Marley Extrusions)*

Plastic pipes have two other advantages compared to clay pipes: they come in long lengths (3 or 6m/10 or 20ft), and can be cut very easily with a fine-toothed saw. The standard size for domestic drains is 110mm, with 160mm used where larger volumes are to be carried, or where the gradient must be shallow. Although smaller sizes are available – to carry only waste water for example – they are not common and would normally only be used to link into a 110mm system

Pipeline installation

Drains should be laid following the recommendations given in BS 5955: Part 6. The trench should be dug as narrow as possible, but not less than 300mm (12in) wide plus the pipe diameter (for 110mm pipe, the minimum trench width would be 410mm/16in) to allow adequate sidefill to be placed. The pipe should be laid and the trench backfilled as soon as possible after the initial excavation. It is essential that the trench sides are adequately supported at all times.

If the material removed from the trench is suitable for use as bedding, the bottom of the trench may be trimmed to form the pipe bed. Otherwise, it must be excavated to a depth that will allow for the specified thickness of imported bedding material below the pipe.

The type and thickness of the bedding should be in accordance with the regulations, and also the recommendations of the building control officer. It should be evenly compacted. Care must be taken to ensure that the bedding is laid to achieve a uniform fall gradient on the pipe.

Small depressions should be made to accommodate the joints, and re-packed after the pipe has been laid to ensure that no voids remain under, or around, the socket. Bricks, or other hard blocks, should not be used as either temporary or permanent supports.

When the bedding has been prepared, the pipes should be laid true to line and level. Each pipe should be checked, and any adjustments made by raising or lowering the bedding to ensure that the pipes are fully supported throughout their length. If a pipe passes

Where rodding points are positioned in gardens, the area surrounding the terminal should be paved, or concreted, to prevent the cover from being buried under grass or soil.

Pipe materials

Traditionally, drainpipes were made of glazed fireclay in short lengths (1m/3ft), with one end plain and the other having a socket to accept the plain end of the adjoining pipe. The joints were sealed with a tarred hemp and, in some cases, covered with a layer of cement mortar. Modern jointing systems for clay pipe are usually of the O-ring type on socketed pipe, or a sleeve and rubber sealing rings on plain pipe.

Fireclay pipes are not easy to cut to length, special cutting tools normally being used by the professional. Alternatively, a disc cutter on a drill can be used (with safety goggles, gloves, etc).

Plastics are the modern alternative to fireclay, normally uPVC. As with uPVC waste systems, they are connected by push-fit, ring-seal joints or solvent welding. Push-fit joints are better, as they allow for movement due to expansion, etc.

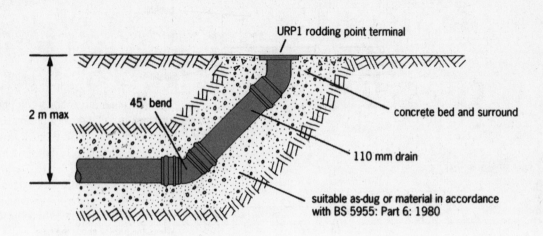

2 m max

URP1 rodding point terminal

45˚ bend

concrete bed and surround

110 mm drain

suitable as-dug or material in accordance
with BS 5955: Part 6: 1980

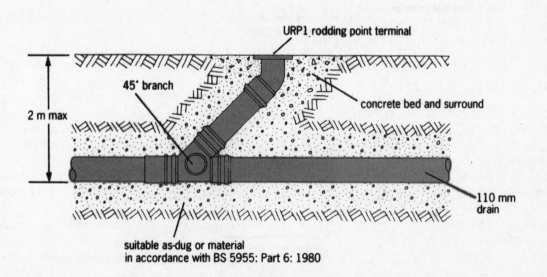

2 m max

URP1 rodding point terminal

45˚ branch

concrete bed and surround

110 mm
drain

suitable as-dug or material
in accordance with BS 5955: Part 6: 1980

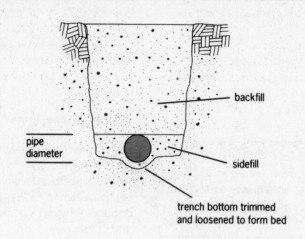

backfill

pipe diameter

sidefill

trench bottom trimmed and loosened to form bed

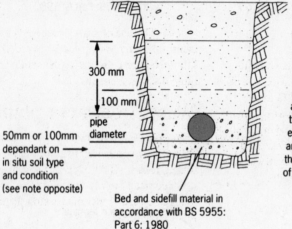

300 mm

100 mm

pipe diameter

50mm or 100mm dependant on in situ soil type and condition (see note opposite)

Bed and sidefill material in accordance with BS 5955: Part 6: 1980

Where the backfill above the pipe contains stones larger than 40mm or where the pipework is deeper than 2m in poor ground, the selected granular material should extend to at least 100mm above the pipe crown. Alternatively the backfill can be graded to eliminate stones exceeding 40mm and this selected backfill used for the first 300mm above the top of the pipe.

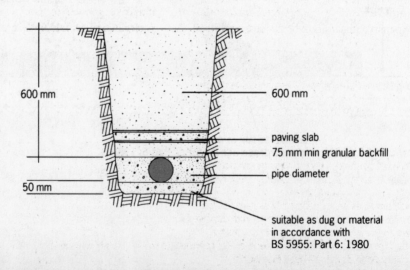

600 mm

50 mm

600 mm

paving slab

75 mm min granular backfill

pipe diameter

suitable as dug or material in accordance with BS 5955: Part 6: 1980

through, or under, the foundation of a building or a wall, a lintel must be built into the wall to provide clearance around the pipe.

Once assembled, the pipeline must be tested for soundness to ensure that there is no leakage. This job is normally carried out by the building control officer or his agent. After the pipe has been tested and approved, the granular sidefill can be added, making sure that it is evenly distributed on both sides of the pipe. Care should be taken to prevent horizontal movement of the pipe, and the material should be packed carefully under the sides to prevent lifting. Any trench supports should be withdrawn in stages to allow the sidefill to be properly compacted.

Next the approved backfill can be placed and hand tamped until a finished layer of 300mm (12in) depth has been placed over the pipe. The main backfill material can then be placed and mechanically tamped.

The foregoing is but a general outline of the required procedure. Details of all aspects should be checked with the relevant authorities before commencing work.

Off-mains sewage

If a mains sewage system is not available, the soil and waste from the property must be handled by a cesspool, septic tank or by a packaged treatment plant (a mini sewage works). The underground system leading to these installations will be the same as for a sewer, with the exception of rainwater disposal. Because rainwater could, and probably would, overload each of these systems, it is normal to discharge it into soakaways dug in the surrounding land and filled with loose rubble.

The cesspool

This is simply a holding tank, which must be emptied frequently, depending on how fast it is filled. Normally, cesspools are sized to require emptying on a monthly basis. This is quite expensive and counterbalances the relatively inexpensive installation of the cesspool itself. A modern cesspool is usually made of glassfibre-reinforced plastic (GRP). It will be placed in a large hole in the ground, and carefully backfilled.

Cesspools are normally only employed where the surrounding ground is unsuitable for accepting the processed effluent discharged from a septic tank or waste treatment plant.

Septic tanks

In principle, the septic tank consists of two linked chambers. One chamber takes the form of an initial settling tank for the solid material, while in the other biological action renders the waste effluent suitable for disposal through a system of perforated pipes laid in nearby ground.

Septic tanks were originally built of block or brick, suitably rendered on the inside with cement mortar. Today, however, they are usually made of GRP. With normal use, a septic tank should need emptying about once every year.

Note The use of strong bleach, or similar agents, to clean sinks and WCs must be avoided because they will kill the bacteria that make the septic tank work – with quite disastrous results.

Waste treatment plants

These are sophisticated effluent treatment units, which range in size upwards from the small, one-property domestic unit. They oxygenate the waste mechanically (an electricity supply is needed), in much the same way as a large sewage works, increasing the natural biological action that breaks it down.

A waste treatment plant is so effective that the output from the unit will be of sufficiently high quality to be acceptable for discharge into a nearby river or stream (with the permission of the river authority). Alternatively, it may be allowed to soak away through a system of perforated pipes laid underground.

Facing page, top *Where the excavated material is suitable, the bottom of the trench may be trimmed to form the pipe bed, and the excavated soil used as sidefill and backfill. (Illustration courtesy Marley Extrusions)*

Facing page, centre *Where the excavated material is not suitable, granular material must be spread evenly on the trench bottom before the pipes are installed. (Illustration courtesy Marley Extrusions)*

Facing page, bottom *Pipes laid at depths of less than 600mm (24in), and not under a road, should be protected from damage by placing over them a layer of concrete slabs, or similar, with a minimum layer of 75mm (3in) cushioning granular material between pipes and slabs. (Illustration courtesy Marley Extrusions)*

Chapter 2

Basic Techniques
Tools and equipment

Gone are the days when a great deal of manual skill was needed to make a satisfactory joint between two lead pipes, or between a lead pipe and a fitting. The development of copper and plastic pipes, and the appropriate fittings, has removed much of the skill from plumbing jobs. As a result, many of the tools required can be found in the household toolkit, or are very inexpensive to purchase. Any special tools needed for more complex installations may be hired.

Cutting tools

Many plumbing jobs involve the cutting of either copper or plastic pipe. For small jobs, both types of pipe can be cut with a hacksaw. The only requirement is to ensure that the pipe is cut square and that any burr is removed from both the inside and outside of the pipe, making certain that no debris falls into the pipe.

If you expect to cut a lot of copper pipe, it would pay to buy a pipe cutter. There are several designs on the market, each with particular attributes. Some versions will cut up to 28mm copper pipe, the largest size likely to be found in any domestic system, and incorporate a useful attachment for de-burring the inside of the pipe. If you need to cut a pipe in a corner, or close to a wall, you can use a hacksaw or a compact cutter. The latter will cut copper pipe of 4-22mm (³⁄₁₆-⁷⁄₈in) diameter, which should cover all normal plumbing work. Its compact size allows cutting in fairly tight corners.

A cutting tool new to the market features a ratchet action. It is ideal for use in awkward situations because only the head rotates around the pipe, the handle being ratcheted back and forth.

Once the pipe has been cut, it is essential to check that the end is square and that there are no burrs. A round or rat-tail file will clean up the inside of the pipe, and a half-round file the outside.

Bending pipe

Although it is quite easy to bend the very small sizes of copper pipe (microbore) by hand, it is not easy to do so without distorting or kinking the pipe, unless a former is used. Also, as microbore comes in coils, it must be straightened before use, which can only be done satisfactorily with the appropriate tool.

Larger sizes of pipe are much more difficult to bend, and much more prone to distortion unless correctly supported. For smallbore (15mm) pipe, a bending spring is slid down inside the pipe and it is bent over the knee. A cord attached to the end of the spring is used to pull it from the pipe. Although 22mm pipe can be bent in the same way, this requires considerable strength, so it is preferable to use a bending machine. These machines will also cope with 28mm copper pipe and stainless steel if required. They are available from tool hire shops.

Cleaning pipe

Cleanliness when making a joint is essential, particularly with soldered joints. Clean copper pipe can be burnished ready for soldering, using an abrasive such as wire wool. Less prone to putting wire slivers in the fingers (and into the pipe, which is not good at all) are circular de-burring tools, or proprietary abrasives such as abrasive tape. With badly-soiled or painted pipe, a wire brush will provide initial rough cleaning.

Joining pipe

Copper pipe may be joined by means of soldered joints or compression fittings. For soldering, a blowlamp is necessary; modern types use gas, and are much cleaner than the old-fashioned paraffin-fuelled versions. For most jobs, the small gas canister units are more than adequate, but for very large jobs, it may be preferable to use a blowtorch with a flexible hose connected to a cylinder of butane or propane gas. An advantage of these units is that the torch can be used in any position, whereas if the canister type is used vertically downwards, there is a danger of flaring.

An essential accessory when using a blowlamp or blowtorch is a (non-asbestos) flameproof mat. Not only will this protect adjacent woodwork and decorations, but it can also be used for picking up hot pipes.

Hot-air guns may also be used for soldering. They usually incorporate a deflector shield that confines the heat to the proximity of the pipe .

Electrically-operated soldering tools are available for hire or purchase. They have the advantage of the heat being confined to the pipe, but because there is no flame, it is easy to forget that the tongs are hot. They must be put on a suitable stand or heatproof mat when not in use.

When working with hot tools, it is a good idea to have a fire extinguisher to hand. Alternatively, a wet towel in a bucket of water can be used to smother a small fire. However, prevention is better than cure, and wood can smoulder for some time before bursting into flames.

Compression joints, and many other plumbing fittings, are secured by tightening nuts. One might expect that most nuts would be of a standard size, but unfortunately this is not the case. Rather than relying on a collection of open-ended spanners, the adjustable spanner is generally used. Several types of adjustable spanner are available, including the girder-pattern and the auto-pattern, but the only really useful version for plumbing is the crescent-pattern spanner. This has angled jaws that can be reversed in the tight corners where pipes are normally found. Two spanners will be needed to tighten or loosen a joint.

Stillsons, or similar wrenches, should not be used on fittings that are to be re-used, as they will damage the faces of the nut. Nor should they be used on copper pipe because they will damage and distort it. Their use should be restricted to gripping steel or galvanised pipe (but they will damage the galvanising), or to situations where adjustable spanners are not effective on damaged parts.

Solder and flux

For end-feed capillary fittings, a supply of solder is needed (solder-ring, or Yorkshire, fittings have the solder built in). To comply with the byelaws, this solder must be of the lead-free type (all solder-ring fittings are lead-free), so it is sensible to specify lead-free solder when making the purchase.

To ensure that the solder seals the joint, flux must be used, and several types are available. Most fluxes are corrosive, so care must be taken to ensure that all excess flux and residue is cleaned from the pipe, otherwise corrosion will occur. Pipes should be flushed out thoroughly before being put into service (particularly in central heating systems).

Jointing tape and compounds

In the past, jointing compound was used in conjunction with hemp on fittings where the seal depended on screw threads being sealed, normally only with galvanised iron pipes for water supply. It is now no longer permitted on the potable water supply, but may be useful on hose union taps for an outside garden supply.

PTFE tape is the modern alternative to the compounds. It comes in a roll, and several layers are wound in a spiral onto the threads to ensure a watertight seal.

Basin/bath spanner

The nuts that hold the taps in place under the rim of a basin or bath are quite difficult to reach, so a special tool is needed. Sometimes called the crowsfoot spanner, the bath/basin spanner incorporates two sizes in the one tool, the larger 18mm (¾in) for bath tap nuts, and the smaller 13mm (½in) for basin taps. For extra leverage (gentle), a metal bar can be used, or a spanner. Too much force could damage the basin or the bath.

An alternative, but more expensive, tool is the basin wrench. This has two sizes of serrated jaw, the head being jointed to the handle to allow movement and, hence,

A ratcheting tube cutter (Ratchcut). As only the head rotates around the pipe, this tool is also suitable for use in confined spaces.

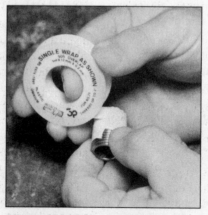

PTFE tape is useful for sealing threaded joints. It should be wound several time around the thread.

A ratcheting flare nut wrench is ideal for use in tight corners. (Photograph courtesy Stanley Tools)

A tile drill bit makes short, clean work of drilling tiles for pipes and screws. (Photograph courtesy Black & Decker)

Stillsons, bath/basin spanner and ratcheting wrench. All may be needed when dealing with compression fittings.

A hired power bender will make light work of bending large-diameter tubes. (Photograph courtesy Ridge Tools)

greater flexibility for reaching into the most inaccessible of corners. An integral tommy bar aids leverage.

Drills

Perhaps one of the more essential tools for plumbing work is an electric drill. A large number of holes must be drilled in walls to pass pipes through, to attach pipe clips, to attach basins or other sanitaryware, and so on. A two-speed or variable-speed electric drill, preferably with hammer action, will make light work of such jobs and can save valuable time. Masonry and plasterboard bits, of the correct sizes, are basic essentials.

The cordless type of drill is the most flexible, but a mains-powered drill with the correct size of extension lead will be more than adequate. A hand drill will be useful for jobs best done at very slow speeds, while a brace and bit may be needed to bore through the substantial timbers to be found in some older properties.

For drilling large holes in walls, a core drill will cut a clean hole of the correct size, which will need the least making good and look neat. It requires a large hammer drill to drive it, but both can be hired.

Lifting floorboards

Floorboards are usually tongued-and-grooved, and it will be necessary to cut through at least one tongue to release the edge of a board. It may then be lifted by inserting a flat, wide tool under the edge and levering. A suitable tool would be a bolster chisel, or a wide (50mm/2in) wood chisel, or a wide tyre lever.

To cut the tongue, a floorboard saw is useful, but even better is a circular saw set so that the blade only just cuts through the tongue and does not protrude below the floorboard. Care should always be taken to avoid any electric cables, or pipes, which may be below the boards.

Screwdrivers

A range of blade and crosshead screwdrivers may be needed, but normally these will be found in the general household toolkit.

Workbench

A surface to work on is always useful, and a portable bench incorporating its own vice will be particularly valuable. However, copper pipe is easily crushed, so care must be taken when holding it in a vice, particularly near the end. The tolerances on both capillary and compression fittings are tight, and a distorted pipe will be difficult, or even impossible, to push into a fitting and seal effectively.

Hiring tools

Unless you intend carrying out a great deal of plumbing work on a regular basis, there will be little point in spending a lot of money on special tools. In any event, these will be readily available from the local hire shop.

Most shops will want to be sure that you have the right tool for the job, and that you know how to use it. Even so, if you are at all uncertain, particularly about safety in use, ask for a demonstration.

You should have a realistic estimate of how long you will need the tool – a day (24 hours), a weekend, a week, or longer. Unless you know you will finish the job in the day, or over the weekend, and can return the tool to the shop within the period, it is sensible to opt for a week's hire. Usually, this is little more than twice the day rate.

Make sure the equipment you hire is clean and in good working order; any damage should be noted at the time of hiring. Tools returned dirty or damaged may cost the hirer part or all of the deposit. Consumable items, such as gas cylinders for blowtorches, will also have to be paid for.

Pipes and fittings

Materials used for pipes carrying hot and cold water within a property range from lead – installed originally – and galvanised iron to the now almost universal copper. Stainless steel is employed in areas where copper is susceptible to corrosion from the water, but this material is much more difficult to bend and join.

Over the years, various attempts have been made to introduce plastic pipes and fittings (the Bartol Acorn System was one; another was Hunter Genova, which is still used in certain commercial installations). However, only with the recent advent of such materials and systems as the Hepworth Hep20, based on polybutylene pipe, and others using cross-linked polyethylene pipe, have plastics begun to replace copper for the water systems in modern properties. Of course, plastics have been used for a number of years in waste systems.

Copper pipes

For many years, copper was used almost exclusively for domestic water supply pipework. Indeed, it is extremely rare nowadays to find lead or galvanised iron water pipes in domestic premises, and where lead is found it should be replaced as soon as possible with a modern alternative.

Until the mid 1970s, copper pipe was sized in imperial dimensions (½, ¾ and 1in), but following metrication, these sizes became 15, 22 and 28mm. This can cause difficulties when joining old imperial-sized pipe to modern metric pipe, because the sizes are not exact equivalents. The old imperial dimensions referred to the inside diameter of the pipe, but the modern metric equivalents specify the outside diameter.

This means that ½in pipe – at 12.7mm internal diameter

– is almost the same as 15mm metric pipe, which means that both compression and capillary metric fittings can be used on both old and new pipe. Unfortunately, this does not apply with ¾ or 1in pipe.

A special adaptor fitting is needed to connect ¾in to 22mm pipe, whether using compression or capillary fittings. When joining 1in to 28mm pipe, however, a metric compression fitting will work, but an adaptor capillary fitting will be needed because of the finer tolerances in this type of joint.

Copper tubing is available in a number of forms – soft, half-hard (bendable) and hard drawn. However, the only types of interest in domestic plumbing are the half-hard temper for 15mm pipe and above (smallbore), and soft temper for 6-12mm pipe (microbore).

Plumbers' merchants sell copper tubing in standard lengths of 3 and 6m (10 and 20ft) for 15mm sizes upwards, but smaller lengths of 1 and 2m (3 and 6ft) are usually available from DIY stores. Soft microbore pipe is usually sold coiled in 10m (33ft) lengths, or longer.

For indoor installation where condensation may occur, and where an attractive appearance is required – such as in the bathroom – copper tubing is also available with a chromium-plated finish. Plastic-coated copper tubing is also available for use in harsh environments. It offers a range of benefits that include: less noise, less condensation, a neat finish that does not require painting, less heat loss and protection from abrasion. Various colours are available, but convention means that yellow is only used for gas piping, blue or green for water, and white for central heating.

Bending copper pipes

Copper tubing in half-hard and soft temper can be bent by hand, using the appropriate tools – internal or external bending springs, or bending machines.

Sizes up to 22mm can be bent with a bending spring, pulling the pipe steadily and firmly round the knee. The spring should be inserted into the pipe so that it supports the whole of the section to be bent; a cord attached to the end allows it to be pulled out of the pipe afterwards. Removing the spring is usually easier if the bend is over-pulled slightly, then pulled back to the correct position. Where the bend must be close to the end of the pipe, it should be made first, then the pipe cut to length.

Being supplied in coils, microbore tubing must be straightened before installation. A microbore tube straightener is the correct tool for this job. Two sizes are available: one for 6 and 8mm sizes, the other for 8 and

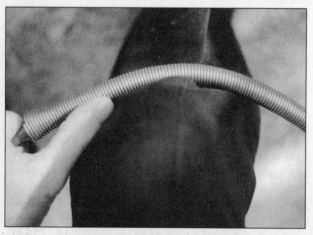

Bending 10mm copper tubing around the knee inside a spring support to prevent kinking.

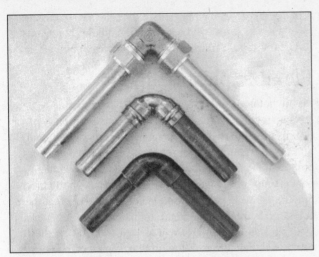

Brass compression, solder-ring and end-feed 90 degree elbows, showing the relative sizes. The bulky compression joint is best used where it will not be seen.

This connector makes cutting into existing pipework easy without draining down. Put the clamp around the pipe, fit the new pipe into the compression tee and hit the boss with a hammer. (Flamco T-plus)

10mm sizes. Select the appropriate hole in the tool and thread the tube through, applying a light lubricating oil if necessary. Once the pipe has been straightened, any bends can be made where needed with a microbore bender in 6/8mm or 10mm sizes as appropriate.

Bending machines vary from small hand tools to large floorstanding units, but for domestic use, most are lightweight and easily portable. It is essential to use the correct former to match the size of the tubing; an oversize former will cause severe rippling, while an undersize former will cause 'throating' constriction. Standard formers usually produce bends to a radius of about three times the pipe diameter.

Bends of 90 degrees are usually made by pulling the operating lever and checking the pipe with a square. An offset bend is made by pulling a bend to the required angle, pushing the pipe further through the machine, turning it through 180 degrees, and pulling another bend. It is essential to ensure that this second bend is in the same plane as the first, and that the ends of the length of pipe are parallel.

Installing pipes

Whether visible or concealed, copper pipes should be adequately supported at regular intervals, using clips designed for the job. The most common, and least expensive, type is the single-screw plastic clip, but the two-piece spacing clip that requires two screws is more traditional. There are many variations of plastic clip, all usually more expensive than the single-screw type. Where pipe is to be hung from beams or supported above the floor – behind the bath panel, for example – double and single split munzing rings should be used.

The maximum spacings for pipe clips are:
- 15mm pipe: 1.2m (4ft) for horizontal runs; 1.8m (6ft) for vertical runs.
- 22mm and 28mm pipe: 1.8m (6ft) for horizontal runs; 2.4m (8ft) for vertical runs.

A rule of thumb for all horizontal runs is to fit a clip every 1m (3ft), and for vertical runs one every 1.5m (5ft). One clip extra is much safer than one clip too few, which can lead to pipes sagging and problems such as airlocks.

If pipe is to run through structural timbers, it is essential that they are not weakened in the process. Notches or holes must be as small as possible, but allow room for expansion. The recommended for size and position are:
- Notches should be no deeper than one eighth of the joist depth, no closer to the bearing end (wall) than $\frac{1}{100}$ of the joist length, and no further from the bearing end than one quarter of the joist length.
- Holes should be drilled in the centre of the joist, no closer to the bearing end than one quarter of the joist length, and no further from the bearing wall than $\frac{1}{10}$ of the length. The maximum hole size should not exceed one quarter of the joist depth.

Accessibility

If pipes are to run in floors or walls, they must remain accessible. This means providing a removable cover along the length of the pipe, or at 2m (6ft) intervals. However, this may be clad with plaster or a tile finish if you wish.

▶ SEE PAGES 50, 52 & 54 FOR STEP-BY-STEP INSTRUCTIONS ON MAKING JOINTS IN COPPER PIPE

Plastic pipe systems

Over the years a number of plastic pipe systems have been introduced for hot and cold water services. Until recently, only one had survived – Hunter Genova – based on a rigid cPVC pipe that cannot be bent. The material can be cut to length with a hacksaw or pipe cutters, while the joints are made by solvent welding.

The two modern flexible plastic pipe materials are polybutylene (used in the Hep20 system) and cross-linked polyethylene (PEX). The latter is widely used in Europe, and is the basis for a number of systems in the UK.

A recent development is a composite plastic and metal pipe (KiTEC), in which an aluminium tube is sandwiched between layers of plastic. This is a rigid pipe, but one that can be bent quite easily by hand.

Plastic pipes must not be joined directly to a boiler; there must be at least 1m (3ft) of copper pipe between the boiler and any plastic pipe.

Solvent welding

Prior to making a joint in cPVC pipe, trim any burrs from the ends of the pipes with a file or sharp knife. Then clean the pipe ends and fitting with solvent cleaner. Brush solvent-weld cement onto the pipe end and push the pipe into the fitting with a twisting motion. The cement

▶ SEE PAGE 56 FOR STEP-BY-STEP INSTRUCTIONS ON MAKING A SOLVENT-WELD JOINT

actually dissolves the plastic, welding the two parts together. The joint will be set within an hour, but it must be left for at least four if the pipe is to carry hot water.

Flexible plastic pipe

Plastic hot and cold water pipes offer a number of advantages. They are not attacked by water or many other chemicals, so they do not corrode. They resist scale build-up in hard water areas, largely because of their smooth bore, which also provides less resistance to flow than occurs with other materials. This, coupled with the fact that the pipe can be bent around corners, means that there is less pressure drop along a run than with other materials.

Plastics do not conduct heat as well as metal, so they can be less dangerous to touch. Plastic pipe can be run like electric cable through joists, which means that far fewer joints are needed than with copper. Joists retain their full strength, because the pipe can pass through holes drilled in the timber rather than notches cut in the surface.

Plastics also inhibit the transmission of sound, which means that there is less intrusive system noise. Because all joints are made cold, there is no need for heat and the attendant fire risk.

However, there are disadvantages, too. One of them is that plastic pipe is flexible and must be supported at much shorter intervals than copper. It sags when heated, and it has a high rate of expansion. When pipes are laid at room temperature, for use at 82°C (28°F), allowance must be made for one per cent expansion.

Polybutylene, cross-linked polyethylene and KiTEC systems are all professional plumbing materials; like copper, they are available through plumbers' merchants.

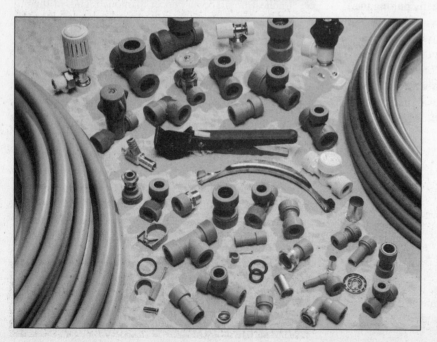

The Hep2O system consists of polybutylene pipe, sized from 10 to 28mm, and a full range of pipe fittings. These include bends, tees, reducers, stopvalves, service valves, etc. Purpose-designed pipe cutters ensure a clean, square cut ready for insertion into the fitting. The system provides everything needed to install a domestic supply network.

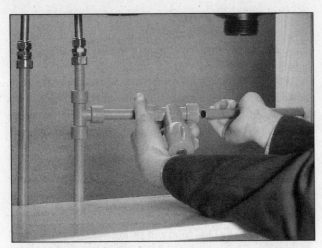

The push-fit fittings used with Hep20 polybutylene pipe make installation quick and simple.

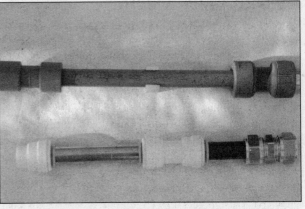

Hep20, Speedfit and brass compression fittings on copper and Hep20 pipe, showing the relative sizes of fitting. Top: non-demountable and demountable Hep20 connectors. Bottom: Speedfit endstop and straight connector with a brass compression fitting.

Only cross-linked polyethylene pipe is available from DIY outlets, and then only in 2m (6ft) lengths. For the professional market, plastic pipes come in coils of 25, 50 and 100m (82, 164 and 328ft), depending on pipe size, as well as straight lengths of up to 6m (20ft).

Polybutylene

Polybutylene pipe is the basis for the Hep20 system, a complete range of fittings and pipes suitable for hot and cold water services, and currently the most common plastic pipe system. The pipe comes in the standard UK metric OD sizes of 10, 15, 22 and 28mm. It is not only designed for use with the system's push-fit fittings, but is also compatible with standard UK metric copper pipe.

The system components include a stoptap, which will connect directly with modern MDPE water supply pipe; alternatively, a polyethylene-to-copper compression stopcock can be used. A range of adaptors, both male and female, is available for connection to a variety of other pipe materials. All fittings incorporate O-rings to make watertight seals. One advantage of these fittings is that the pipe may be rotated easily inside the fitting without causing any leakage from the joint.

Hep20 fittings have been designed to form reliable joints with copper pipes. Care should be taken when joining to copper to make sure that the pipe is cut square and is free from burrs or swarf, which could damage the O-ring. A pipe cutter, which rounds the end of the pipe slightly, will ensure freedom from external burrs.

With imperial sizes of copper pipe, the 15 and 28mm fittings will make satisfactory connections without difficulty, but for connection to ¾in copper pipe, a special O-ring is needed to adapt the 22mm demountable fittings to form a satisfactory joint.

Hep20 fittings cannot be connected directly to chrome-plated copper or stainless steel pipe. With the former, either a standard compression fitting should be used, or the plating must be stripped to expose the copper, and the Hep20 fitting installed as normal. With stainless steel, a compression fitting must be employed.

Standard compression fittings can be used with Hep20 pipe, but when making a joint, it is essential to fit a metal insert to the end of the pipe, as it provides support for the pipe against the olive. Ensure that the pipe is pushed fully into the fitting, and that the point of compression, under the olive, is within the length of the insert. PTFE tape applied over the compression ring will assist jointing. The fitting should be tightened about 1½ turns from the point where the compression ring is felt to grip the pipe.

Oil-based jointing compounds, or flux, should never be used with Hep20, even when connecting to other types of pipe or compression fittings. The pipe will not rotate in standard compression fittings after tightening.

Because Hep20 pipe expands considerably as the temperature rises, it will tend to sag along its length. This is unacceptable on long exposed runs, but there are two solutions: one is to box it in so that it is completely hidden; the other is to replace it with a length of copper pipe in those areas where exposure is unavoidable.

Although this pipe is resistant to attack from the chemicals in concrete, etc, the Water Byelaws demand that all such pipes should be accessible. One way to achieve this is to use a pipe-in-pipe system, where the pipe carrying the water is run through a pipe of larger diameter and can be pulled out in case of a problem.

▶ **SEE PAGE 58 FOR STEP-BY-STEP INSTRUCTIONS ON USING POLYBUTYLENE PIPE FITTINGS**

PEX pipe

Cross-linked polyethylene pipe is used in a number of systems, but in two size ranges: the UK standard sizes of 12,15, 22 and 25mm OD; and European sizes of 14, 16, 20 and 25mm OD. The pipe and fittings of these two systems are not compatible with each other.

The UK pipe system uses standard brass compression fittings (plus inserts), or push-fit fittings such as Speedfit, which are used on copper pipe. The other system, however, uses patented fittings. With these, a range of special adaptors is needed to provide a connection to UK-sized compression fittings, such as valves, etc, and hence to copper pipe or other plastic pipes.

The easy way to distinguish which sizes of pipe are installed is to measure the outside diameter. Most sizes are sufficiently different to be easily distinguished, except the 15 and 16mm sizes, which need careful measurement. However, most pipes have the name and size printed on the outside. Another clue to the pipe size comes from the fittings used, which normally are marked with the size.

Some of the more unusual systems are only installed by a limited number of companies, and the fittings or adaptors for them may not be generally available – even from plumbers' merchants. If the system installed in your property is identified as one that is not readily available, you will need to contact the manufacturer, or installer, for advice on its extension or modification.

Joining PEX pipe

When using Speedfit fittings, joining PEX pipe is simply a matter of cutting the end square with the proper plastic pipe cutters, fitting the support insert into the pipe end, and pushing the pipe into the fitting past the O-ring. To release the pipe, the collar is simply pushed back towards the joint and the pipe pulled out (a special key will help, but it is not essential).

To join PEX pipe with compression fittings is equally simple. Cut the pipe square, place the nut and compression olive on the end of the pipe, fit the support to the pipe, push the pipe into the fitting, and tighten the nut with a spanner in the usual way. Neither sealing compounds nor PTFE tape are required when making Speedfit or compression joints on PEX pipe.

KiTEC system

The composite KiTEC pipe and fitting system is unique and not compatible with any UK size of pipe or fitting. It combines the best features of the aluminium and plastic components to form a pipe that is light, strong and unaffected by corrosion.

By combining the two materials, the thermal expansion and sagging disadvantages of plastic pipes are avoided, while flexibility, frost resistance and ease of use are retained. Once bent, the pipe keeps its set, unlike plastic which relaxes back. It is easily formed into curves by hand, and into tight bends, using a bending spring.

It clips like copper, and expands like copper, but is less than half the weight. Another advantage over plastics is the ability to use metal locating devices when the pipe is buried in walls or floors. Pipe sizes range from 1014 (10mm ID/14mm OD), through 1216 and 1620, to 2025. To identify this system, the pipe is marked with the size (e.g. 1216 XLPE). The fittings are also marked.

The fitting design is a combination of compression and double O-ring configuration. To make a joint, the pipe

To make a Speedfit joint, simply push the pipe fully into the fitting; the pipe can be removed after pushing on the collar.

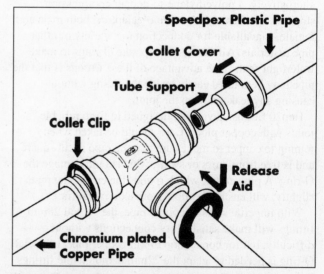

The components of a typical Speedfit fitting. A metal support insert must be fitted to plastic pipe before pushing into the fitting.

end should be bevelled so that it can be pushed through the O-rings, using the special bevelling tool. Then the nut is placed over the end, the pipe pushed into the fitting and the nut tightened in the usual way.

The fittings are re-usable, but the O-rings must be replaced each time. The only tools needed are an adjustable spanner, special KiTEC bevelling tool and KiTEC bending springs. Adaptors are needed to link this system to copper pipe or brass compression fittings.

Pipe-in-pipe systems

In some modern properties, the hot and cold water supply pipes may be buried in the floor and/or walls, each passing through another protective pipe sleeve. This allows a damaged pipe to be replaced by disconnecting it at both ends and pulling it out (not forgetting to pull a new piece of pipe into place at the same time).

With such systems (almost invariably mains pressure systems), it is usual to run just one hot and one cold pipe to each location, and to take the pipes to each appliance from a manifold set in the wall. The terminations for these pipes are usually fixed in the wall, and the terminal fittings (such as taps) screwed directly into them.

These systems are not easy to modify once installed, since all the piping is put in place as the property is being constructed and not afterwards. However, the manifold is usually accessible, under a cover, and may have spare, blanked-off outlets. Even so, pipe runs will be difficult to install without major work.

Lead pipe

Properties built before about 1940, and not since modernised, may still have lead pipework. This is an unsatisfactory situation for a number of reasons: in soft water areas, the lead is likely to contaminate drinking water; in hard water areas, the pipes will be prone to scaling up. Lead pipe is not easy to tap into, and the entire system will offer poor performance by virtue of it being so old. Further installation of lead pipe is prohibited.

The best thing to do is to remove the entire system, and replace it with a modern design, using copper or plastic pipe. It is highly likely that the service pipe from the mains to the house will also be of lead, and could still contaminate the drinking water if left in situ. Therefore, it would be sensible to contact the local water company and have it replaced at the same time as the rest of the system.

It is not a good idea to replace pipes and not, at the same time, replace galvanised cisterns, etc, in an effort to save money. In a galvanised water cistern over 15 years old, corrosion below the water line can cause catastrophic failure. It is unlikely to be covered properly, and will contain dust and dead insects, or worse. A modern tank will ensure a clean supply of water and will not corrode.

It is much easier to build a new system than to try to link into old components. This also presents an opportunity to provide better performance from a more modern system.

Electrical bonding

When using plastic pipes or plastic fittings with copper pipe, the electrical bonding continuity to earth with be lost. To comply with the Wiring Regulations, it is essential that all metal parts are bonded to earth. If necessary, this should be achieved by running separate earth wires wherever plastic pipe is fitted, and by bridging across plastic fittings between copper pipes.

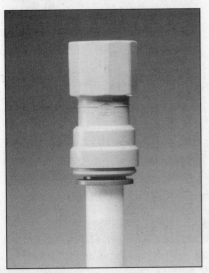

The Speedfit tap connector slips onto the pipe and screws by hand onto the tap tail.

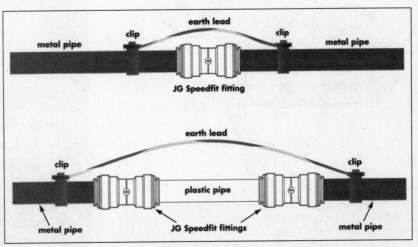

The practice of using metal pipework for earthing has been discontinued in the UK. However, when Speedfit or other plastic fittings form a break in the continuity of the existing metal pipework, which may have been used for earthing or bonding, the electrical continuity should be reinstated by fixing a bonding lead permanently to the pipe.

Making a compression joint

When it comes to joining copper pipes, there are two traditional methods to choose from: compression fittings and capillary fittings. The latter require more skill to install, but the former are bulkier. Whereas a capillary fitting relies on a layer of solder to make a watertight seal with a pipe, a compression fitting makes a simple mechanical joint, pressing a soft metal ring – known as an olive – tightly against both pipe and joint socket.

There is a wide range of compression fittings to choose from, including straight couplers, elbows, reducers, tees and endstops. In addition, a variety of special fittings are only available in compression form. These include stoptaps, gate valves and tank connectors.

Although it may seem unlikely, compression fittings need no additional jointing paste, tape or sealer to make a watertight joint. However, a thin smear of Fernox Leak Sealer may ease the making of the joint by acting as a lubricant. In the case of a scored pipe, it will also fill the gap and provide the seal that the olive will not be capable of providing under such circumstances. If a pipe is damaged to this extent, it may be wiser to remove the damaged portion back to sound material and insert a new section.

TOOLS AND MATERIALS
☐ Tape measure
☐ Pencil
☐ Pipe cutter or hacksaw
☐ Adhesive tape
☐ Half-round or flat file
☐ Rat-tail file
☐ Wire wool or abrasive tape
☐ Wire brush (possibly)
☐ Adjustable spanners
☐ Copper pipe
☐ Compression fitting

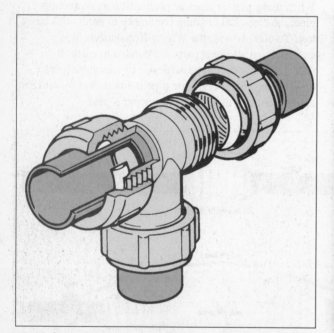

Compression fittings are invariably made of brass, and are more expensive than soldered fittings. However, they are ideal where it may be inconvenient or even dangerous to use a blowtorch for soldering. They also allow joints to be re-made with relative ease. When the capnut is tightened onto the fitting, it compresses a metal ring (the olive) against the pipe and the end of the fitting, providing an effective watertight seal.

3 Clean the end of the pipe using wire wool or a proprietary abrasive, aiming for a good shine. A wire brush may be needed if the pipe has been painted or is badly tarnished. An olive is unlikely to make a good seal on such a pipe.

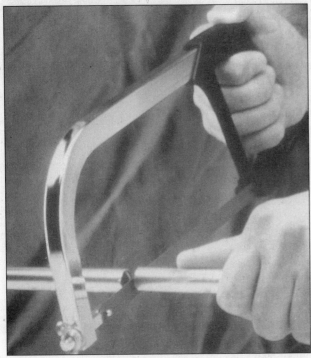

1 Cut the pipe to length with a pipe cutter or a hacksaw, as shown here. A piece of adhesive tape wrapped around the pipe, with its edges aligned, will help ensure that the cut is square when using a hacksaw.

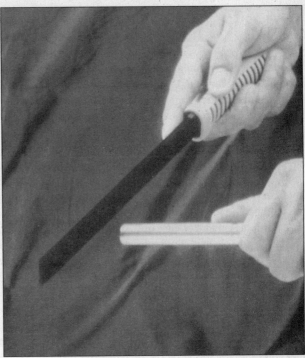

2 Any burr on the cut end must be removed; use a flat file around the outside, and a round file for the inside. Don't allow filings to fall into the pipe. If they are transported round the system, they may cause corrosion or damage valves, etc.

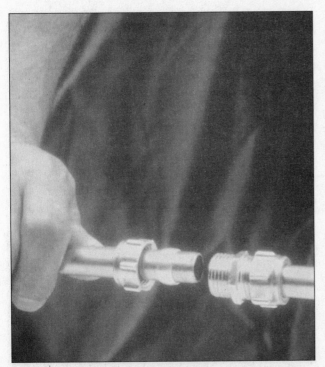

4 Remove the capnut from the fitting, sliding it onto the pipe, followed by the olive. Push the pipe firmly into the fitting until it reaches the end stop. Then screw the nut onto the fitting so that it is finger tight.

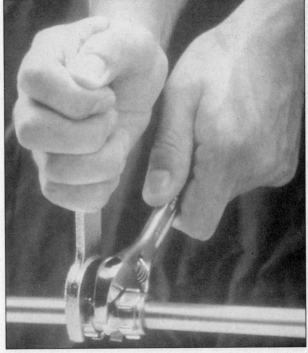

5 Tighten the joint by turning the nut 1½ turns, using two spanners together. The joint should now be sealed. However, if it leaks, a further half-turn should suffice. Do not over-tighten, as this can lead to the joint leaking.

Making a solder-ring joint

Soldered capillary joints may be made using either solder-ring or end-feed fittings. Both need skill to install correctly, but the former are easier to use than the latter, although they are more expensive. In both cases, the solder is melted by a blowtorch, or a hot-air gun, and will flow between fitting and pipe, bonding the two together permanently.

As the name implies, solder-ring fittings contain an integral 'ring' of solder at each pipe socket, and require no further solder to be added when making the joint. Originally, all solders were based on lead, but since this material must be kept out of water systems, solder-ring fittings from UK manufacturers, and most others, now only contain lead-free solder.

As with making a compression joint, the end of the pipe must be cut square, de-burred and cleaned thoroughly. Cleanliness is essential if the solder is to provide a watertight seal, and to this end a chemical cleaner, known as flux, should be applied to both fitting and pipe prior to heating. The action of the heat will cause the flux to bubble, removing any grease from the metal.

The joint should be heated sufficiently for a bright ring of solder to appear at the mouth of the fitting, and then the heat removed quickly. Overheating will cause the solder to run out of the joint, allowing it to leak and leaving an unsightly blob of solder on the pipe or fitting. There is more than enough solder in the fitting to make a secure joint – there is no need to feed in more solder, which may partially, or even completely, block the pipe.

TOOLS AND MATERIALS

- [ ] Tape measure
- [ ] Pencil
- [ ] Pipe cutter or hacksaw
- [ ] Adhesive tape
- [ ] Half-round or flat file
- [ ] Rat-tail file
- [ ] Wire wool or abrasive tape
- [ ] Round wire brush
- [ ] Brush
- [ ] Flux
- [ ] Blowtorch
- [ ] Cleaning cloth
- [ ] Copper pipe
- [ ] Solder-ring capillary fitting

To ensure a watertight soldered joint, the pipe must fit tightly in the socket of the fitting. When heat is applied to the end of the fitting, the ring of solder melts and flows around the end of the pipe, bonding the two components together when it cools.

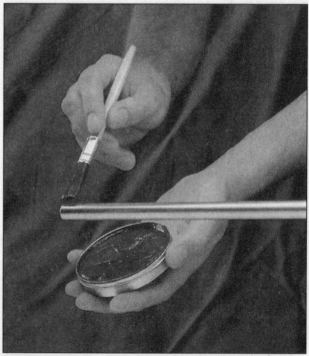

3 Brush a thin film of flux onto the outside of the pipe, as well. Even the grease from your fingers will prevent a good soldered joint, so it is not worth taking chances. Use a non-corrosive flux in paste form.

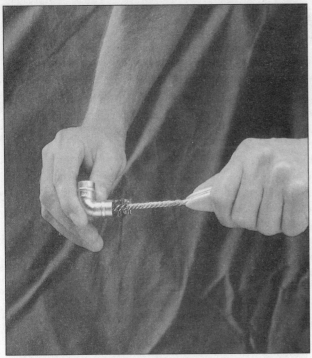

1 Cut the pipe to length, making sure that the end is square, and deburr the cut edges inside and out. Clean the outside of the pipe with wire wool, and the inside of the fitting with a wire brush to ensure that the surface will flux correctly.

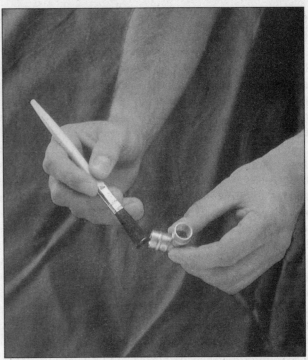

2 Brush a thin film of flux on the inside of the fitting. The flux acts as a chemical cleaner, ensuring that both pipe and fitting are perfectly clean so that the solder can make a good bond with the metal.

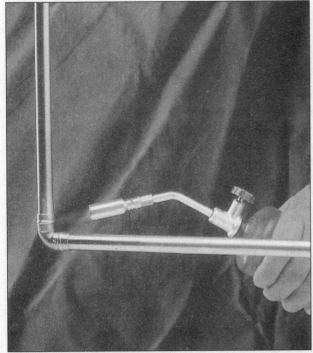

4 Push the pipe into the fitting as far as it will go; it is a good idea to mark the depth on the pipe before assembly. Then heat the pipe and fitting slowly until a ring of solder 'flashes' around the end of the fitting. Remove the heat immediately.

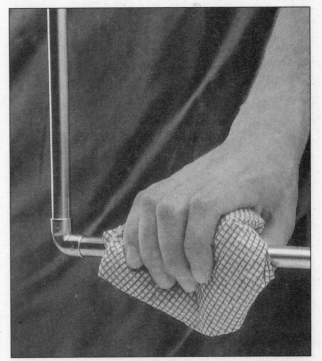

5 The joint is now made, and should be allowed to cool. Wipe the outside of the pipe and fitting clean of excess flux. When installing solder-ring fittings, take care only to heat one end at a time, otherwise solder may run from the wrong end.

Making an end-feed joint

Unlike solder-ring fittings, end-feed capillary fittings have no added solder, and the joint must be made by feeding solder into the end of the (heated) fitting. When the pipe and fitting are at the correct temperature, touching the end of the solder wire onto the junction between them will cause the solder to melt and be drawn into the joint by capillary action.

Solder containing lead is not permitted to be used on potable water supplies. Always ask for lead-free solder when buying supplies to avoid using a lead-based solder by mistake. If such a mistake is made, the installation inspected and the mistake discovered, the entire system will have to be dismantled and rebuilt using lead-free solder. In addition, you may be prosecuted and fined under the Water Byelaws. It is much better to avoid such a possibility by simply using lead-free solder, which is also less hazardous to health.

Using end-feed fittings successfully – and neatly – requires some skill, but since the fittings are cheaper than solder-ring types, if you have a lot of joints to make, it would be worth making an attempt to acquire that skill. One difficulty is judging the amount of solder to feed into the joint – too little will result in a leaking joint; too much will produce an unsightly finish covered in hard blobs. As a rough guide, the length of solder wire needed will be approximately equal to the diameter of the pipe.

TOOLS AND MATERIALS

- ☐ Tape measure
- ☐ Pencil
- ☐ Pipe cutter or hacksaw
- ☐ Adhesive tape
- ☐ Half-round or flat file
- ☐ Rat-tail file
- ☐ Wire wool or abrasive tape
- ☐ Small round wire brush
- ☐ Brush
- ☐ Flux
- ☐ Lead-free solder wire
- ☐ Blowtorch
- ☐ Cleaning cloth
- ☐ Copper pipe
- ☐ End-feed capillary fitting

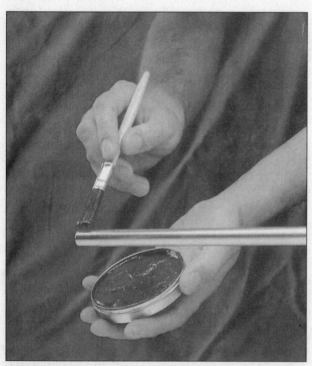

3 Brush more flux onto the outside of the pipe, keeping it out of the pipe as much as possible. All the pipework should be flushed through thoroughly after installation to remove all traces of flux and dirt.

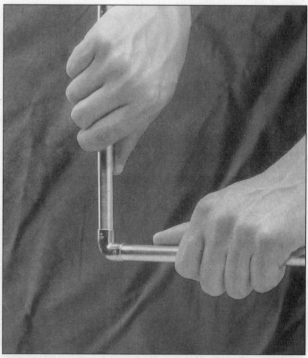

4 Having previously measured and marked the amount of pipe that should be inserted into the fitting, assemble the joint. Push the pipe in to it mark, twisting it slightly to ensure a good distribution of the flux.

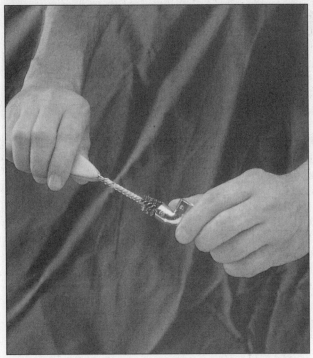

1 In many respects, making an end-feed capillary joint is the same as making a solder-ring joint. Having cut, de-burred and cleaned the pipe, clean the inside of the fitting thoroughly with a small wire brush.

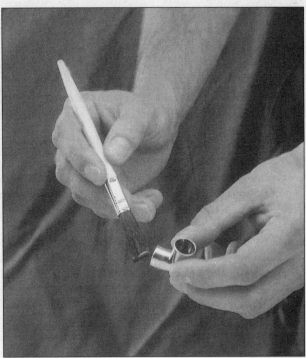

2 Prepare the fitting for soldering by brushing a thin film of flux around the inside of the pipe socket. Treat both sockets if you intend adding a second pipe to the fitting at the same time. Keep the flux off your fingers.

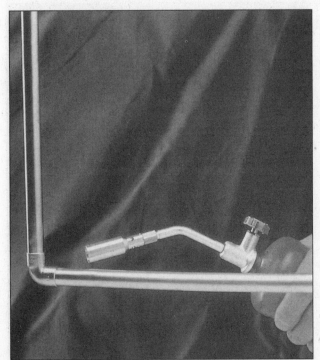

5 Apply heat to the pipe, playing the flame of the blowtorch just beside the fitting and onto the fitting itself. Remove the heat from time to time and touch the end of the solder wire onto the heated pipe. When hot enough, the solder will melt.

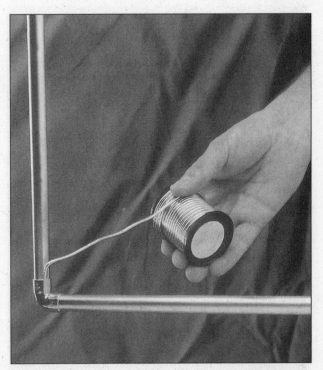

6 Apply the solder to the junction of the pipe and fitting, where it will melt and run into the joint. The ring will 'flash' around the junction to show that the joint has been completed. Thoroughly clean the pipe and fitting of flux and residue.

Making a solvent-weld joint

Although some plastic water supply pipes make use of solvent-welded joints, the technique is much more common for soil and waste pipe systems. However, the method used is essentially the same for both. The step-by-step sequence here shows a 110mm soil pipe being joined to another length of pipe by means of a straight coupler.

As with all pipework, the pipes must be cut to length with their ends square so that they will butt up against the fitting's integral stop. Adhesive tape or even a sheet of paper can be wrapped around the pipe with its edges aligned to provide a square cutting guide. Rather than cutting straight down through the pipe, you will find it easier if you just break through the pipe wall, then roll it away from you and cut down through the wall again. Continue in this way until you have a cut that runs all the way round the pipe.

Having cleaned up the end of the pipe, check its fit in the fitting's socket, and make alignment marks with a pencil if the fitting is directional. Depending on the adhesive used, it may also pay you to mark the amount of the pipe that is inserted in the socket, so that you know where to apply the cement.

In some cases, it is necessary to remove the glaze from the parts before applying the cement, using wire wool. This will be specified by the cement manufacturer. Make sure the solvent-weld cement is the correct type for the pipe and fittings being used. Your supplier will be able to advise you.

TOOLS AND MATERIALS
☐ Tape measure
☐ Pencil
☐ Fine-tooth saw
☐ Half-round file
☐ Absorbent paper
☐ Solvent-weld cement
☐ Waste pipe
☐ Solvent-weld fitting

SAFETY FIRST

Although making solvent-weld joints in both supply and waste pipework is a simple process, the solvent-weld cement can be hazardous. When using this material, follow this safety code:

● Solvent-weld cement gives off powerful fumes, so take care not to inhale them.
● Work in a well-ventilated space.
● Never smoke while using solvent-weld cement; the fumes may become poisonous if inhaled through a cigarette.
● Keep solvent-weld cement off your skin. If you should accidentally come into contact with the cement, wash it off immediately.
● Keep the solvent cement away from children. When not in use, store it in a locked cupboard.
● Take care not to spill the solvent cement onto the face of the pipe or fitting, as it will leave an unsightly mark. Keep it away from other plastics as well.
● Always read and follow the manufacturer's instructions to ensure safe use.

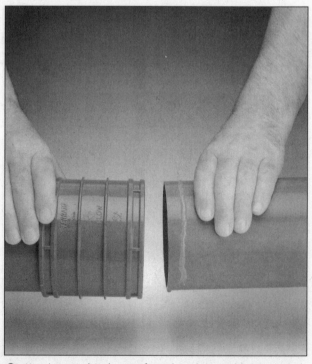

3 Keeping your hands away from the solvent-weld cement, push the pipe firmly into the socket of the fitting until it comes up against the integral stop. Most solvent-weld fittings are provided with this feature.

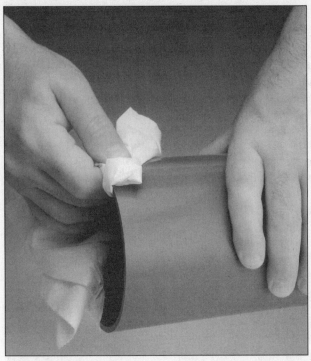

1 Cut the pipe to length with a fine-tooth saw, making sure that the end is square. Remove any burrs with a file. Then, using clean absorbent paper, wipe both mating surfaces thoroughly to remove any moisture, dirt and grime.

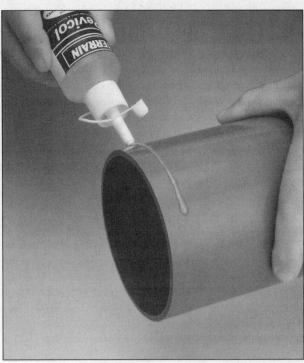

2 Apply a thin bead of proprietary solvent-weld cement around the end of the pipe and to the inside of the fitting's socket. This should be about 3mm (⅛in) in from the end of the pipe and the edge of the socket.

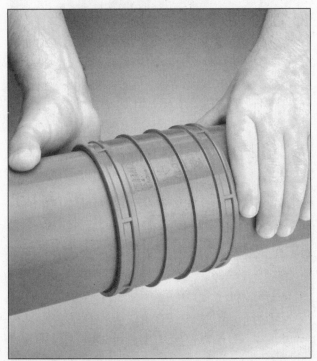

4 Twist the pipe to ensure that the solvent-weld cement spreads evenly around the joint, ensuring a watertight seal. Adjust the positions of any directional fittings before the resistance of the cement becomes too great.

5 Excess solvent cement may ooze from the joint as the pipe and fitting are pushed together. Wipe this carefully with a piece of clean absorbent paper to remove it from the exposed pipework and leave a neat finish.

Making polybutylene joints

Joining sections of polybutylene pipe with push-fit fittings is a very simple and quick operation. The pipe itself should only be cut with the purpose-made, secateur-type cutters, which leave a clean, square cut ready for jointing. The latter is simple, the fittings incorporating O-ring seals and stainless steel grab rings. Two versions of fitting are available: re-usable demountable, and the slimmer non-demountable type.

When making a joint, a metal insert is pushed into the end of the pipe to support it. Then the pipe is pushed, with a slight twist, into the fitting to the

Jointing procedure

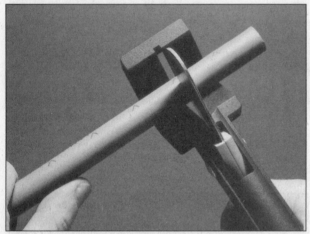

1 Cut the pipe to length, using one of the cutting/insertion marks printed on the pipe as a guide. The cut should be made with the special Hep20 pipe cutters, which act like secateurs and will ensure a square cut.

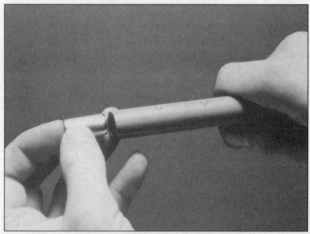

2 Ensure that the pipe is free from burrs, and insert a support tube. If connecting Hep20 fittings to existing copper pipe, it is particularly important to remove all burrs from that pipe. To this end, it is preferable to use a pipe cutter rather than a saw.

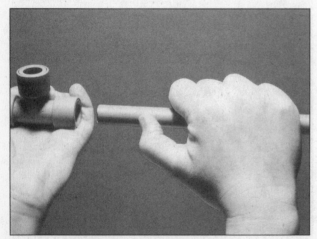

3 The cutting mark on the pipe and the insertion mark on the fitting are useful guides to ensure that a joint is correctly made with the pipe pushed fully home. Each fitting is pre-lubricated and ready for use.

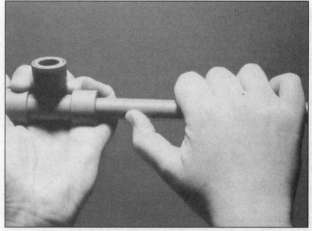

4 Push the pipe into the fitting until you reach full socket depth. Hold the fitting and pipe firmly, then tug back to ensure that an effective joint has been made. If a directional fitting has been used, it can be rotated to face in the correct direction.

second point of resistance. All the O-ring seals in the fittings are pre-lubricated during assembly, so additional lubrication is not normally required. However, if a demountable fitting is being re-used, it may be necessary to add more silicone lubricant.

Whichever type of fitting is being used, either demountable or non-demountable, the same procedure should be adopted for making a joint. If a demountable type needs to be dismantled to allow alterations to the pipework, this is easily achieved by simply unscrewing its retaining cap and pulling the pipe free. Then, after removing and discarding the grab ring, the remaining components can be slipped from the pipe and re-assembled (with a new grab ring) in the body of the fitting, allowing it to be used again.

TOOLS AND MATERIALS

- ☐ Tape measure
- ☐ Marker pen
- ☐ Pipe cutters
- ☐ Pliers
- ☐ Polybutylene pipe
- ☐ Push-fit fittings
- ☐ Support tubes
- ☐ New grab rings
- ☐ Silicone lubricant

Removing a demountable fitting

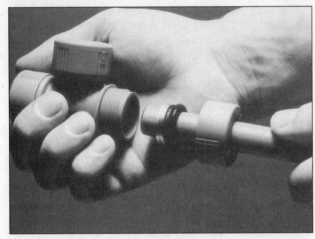

1 To dismantle a demountable fitting, begin by unscrewing the retaining cap. Slide this back along the pipe, then pull the pipe clear of the fitting. Place the fitting to one side, as you will be able to re-use it.

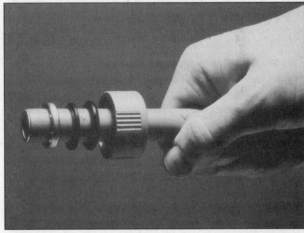

2 The O-ring, spacer washer and grab ring will be left in place on the end of the pipe. Slide the O-ring and spacer away from the grab ring. You will not be able to retrieve them until you have removed the grab ring.

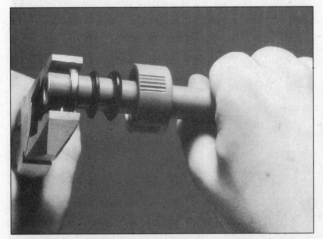

3 Flatten the teeth on the grab ring by squeezing it with a pair of pliers. This will enable all components to be removed from the pipe. Once removed, the used grab ring must be discarded and never re-used.

4 To re-assemble the fitting, simply insert a new grab ring together with the spacer washer and O-ring into the fitting. Replace the retaining cap and lubricate the O-ring with the correct silicone Lubricant. The fitting is ready to be re-used.

Earth bonding

At one time, it was common practice for the plumbing system to be used as the earth conductor for the electrical system in a property. The pipework was particularly suitable for this purpose because, being lead, all the pipes were joined electrically, either through wiped joints or brass fittings, while the water supply pipe into the property was buried in the earth. So the all-metal system, in good contact with the ground, provided an excellent failsafe in the event of a fault occurring in an electrical appliance or circuit.

Earthing

The earth can be considered as a large conductor, which is at zero potential. The purpose of earthing is to connect together all metalwork, other than that designed to carry current, to earth so that dangerous potential differences cannot exist between different metal parts or between metal parts and earth. For example, earthing will prevent voltage differences between an electric washing machine and the water pipes, or a radiator and a refrigerator.

By connecting all metalwork, a path is provided for leaking current, which can be detected and/or interrupted by a fuse, circuit breaker or residual current device. The system commonly used is called 'earth equipotential bonding'. Its objective is to join together with a conductor (called a protective conductor) all exposed metalwork, the appliances connected to the electrical installation, and metalwork in the building that is in contact with earth (such as pipes, taps, baths, sinks, etc) to a main earthing terminal. Nowadays, this terminal is normally provided by the local electricity supply company, but where the supply is by overhead cable, the earth may be provided by a copper rod driven into the ground.

If, for example, the casing of an electrical appliance was to become 'live' because of a loose wire inside, the current could flow harmlessly to earth through the protective conductor to which it is connected, tripping the circuit breaker or blowing the fuse. If the casing was not earthed, and it was touched, the current would pass through the body to earth, giving a potentially lethal electric shock. To prevent this possibility, all exposed conductive parts should be connected to the earthed point of the source of supply via protective conductors at the main earthing terminal.

Main equipotential bonding conductors connect together, and to earth, mains water pipes, gas pipes, service pipes and ducting, central heating, exposed metallic parts of the structure, and any lightning protection system. Supplementary bonding conductors are installed wherever a person may make simultaneous contact with an electrical appliance (e.g. a kettle) and other metalwork, such as the taps.

In practical terms, this means that all metal parts, particularly of the plumbing system, must be earth bonded. For supplementary bonding, $4mm^2$ cable and earth clips to BS 951 should be used and fitted with appropriate labels.

With modern systems, it is essential to check that the conductor path is not interrupted by a plastic pipe or fitting (some plastic fittings have conductors built in to ensure continuity). Every such gap must be bridged – it is all too easy to forget that bath taps, connected to the supply by plastic pipe, need earth bonding when the tap tails under the bath are hidden behind a bath panel.

Standard earth pipe clamp (which should be clearly labelled: 'Safety electrical connection – do not remove').

Copper water supply pipes earth bonded with a length of copper wire, fixed between a pair of earth clamps.

Earth bonding copper strip built into a plastic shower stoptap. The compression nuts are of plated brass.

Right *Supplementary bonding conductors in the kitchen link the pipes to the kitchen taps, the sink (metal) and the earth terminal of the waste disposal unit, which is linked to the domestic earth.*

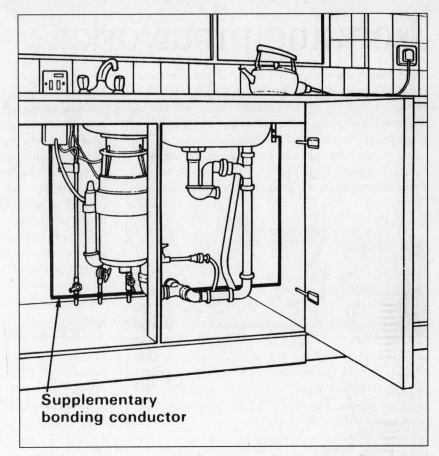

**Supplementary
bonding conductor**

Below *In the bathroom, supplementary earth bonding conductors must link the metal parts of the shower waste, metal pipes, bath taps (if pipes are plastic), bath waste, washbasin waste, any exposed metal water pipe (including central heating) and any electrical appliance to earth.*

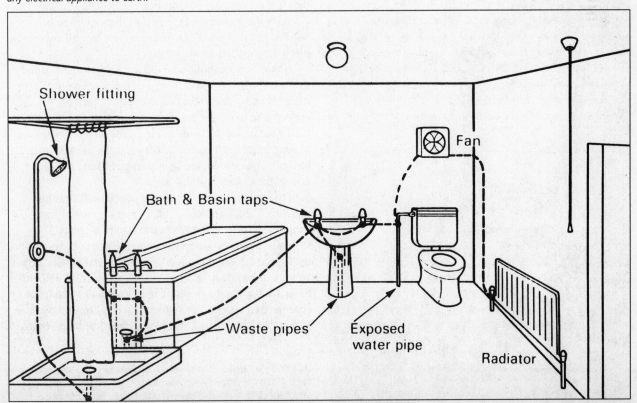

Shower fitting

Fan

Bath & Basin taps

Waste pipes

Exposed
water pipe

Radiator

Isolating pipework

The smooth completion of any project depends on good planning and organisation, having all the materials needed to hand, with the right tools available, and a clear idea of the sequence of events. An essential aspect of good planning is to ensure that if anything goes wrong, the entire system is not out of action while the problem is solved. It is partly for this reason that current Water Byelaws insist on the use of servicing valves at important outlets so that only the outlet needs to be turned off for repair, and not the whole system.

If it is not appropriate to fit servicing valves where pipes are cut, for example when replacing a bath in a new position, the old pipes may be quickly stopped off (Speedfit endstops are ideal for this), and the water turned on again to bring the rest of the system back into operation. Then the work can be completed, leaving the pipe connections until last and keeping the amount of time when the system is out of action to the minimum.

Most products come with full fitting instructions, including details specific to the product. Before starting the job, you should read these and make sure you understand them fully. Then check that all components have been supplied.

Turn off the supply

Modern plumbing systems should have a servicing valve close to each outlet. In addition, valves (usually gate valves, but they could also be stopvalves) should be fitted to the supply pipes from the cistern or storage tank, and there should be a stoptap on the rising main where it enters the property. It is important to know where to turn off the supply to the plumbing (and heating) systems so that fast action can be taken in an emergency, or to simplify the isolation of the part of the system to be worked on. It is good practice to ensure that all valves and pipes are labelled appropriately.

To work on an appliance with servicing valves, simply turn these off and leave the rest of the system on. Where there are only gate valves on the system, turn off the valve appropriate to the section to be worked on, but leave the main stoptap on. If there are no valves on the system, the stoptap itself must be turned off or, if the work is on a low-pressure system fed by a storage cistern, tie up the arm of the cistern ball valve.

In the unlikely absence of a stopcock on the rising main, or if the stopcock is totally seized, the only way the supply can be turned off is at the water company's stopvalve, usually located close to the house boundary in the adjacent footpath or road, under a metal cover. This valve will be about 1m (3ft) below ground, and will either have a T-bar handle or a square metal shank. The latter type needs a special key (which you can hire or buy from a plumbers' merchant); the former may just be reachable

A key for the outside stop valve may be essential if no stop valve is fitted inside the property. You can buy one from a plumbers' merchant, or may be able to make one from a length of wood.

by hand, but if not, a notched piece of timber with a T-piece at the top may do the job.

In an emergency, or if all else fails, call the emergency number of the local water company and ask them to turn off the water for you. However, a much better solution, if you have no mains stopvalve in the property or if the existing valve is unusable, is to have a professional plumber or the local water company fit a new stopvalve inside the house.

To drain down the section of pipework, attach a hosepipe to the appropriate drain valve outlet, run the hose to a nearby gully, and open the valve with a spanner. Don't forget to close the valve again before doing the work, as it is easy to forget to close it after the work has been completed.

Work can be done on parts of the pipework by:

- Turning off the mains stopvalve and running the kitchen cold tap (internal mains supply).
- Emptying the cold cistern by turning on the cold bath tap with the ball valve tied up. The hot cylinder will stay full if there is no flow to it from the storage tank. It should be drained from its own drain valve only if work needs to be done on the cylinder itself, or to pipework leading to or from it.

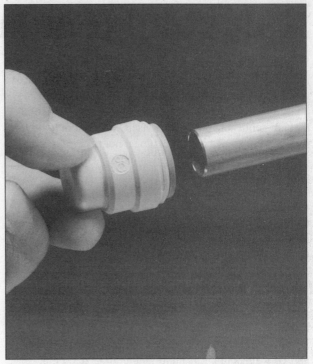

The Speedfit endstop simply slips onto the cut end of a pipe to form a leakproof seal. It is ideal for capping a pipe temporarily while work is carried out on that section.

A stoptap should be fitted to the rising main, close to the point at which it enters the property. This will allow the supply to the whole plumbing system to be shut off.

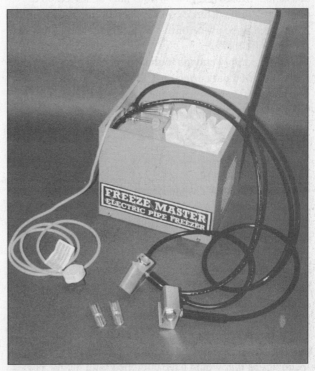

If gate valves are not fitted to a section of pipework, an electric freezing machine can isolate the section for as long as it takes to complete the job. (Hire Shops)

Rules and regulations

With the exceptions of gas work and the installation of unvented hot water systems, there is no legal requirement for anyone carrying out plumbing work to be suitably qualified. However, there are many rules and regulations that are applicable to the work itself, which should be followed. In some cases, it is illegal not to comply with them. The main groups of regulations that apply to plumbing work are:

● Water Byelaws
● Building Regulations
● Gas Safety Regulations
● IEE Wiring Regulations

Water Byelaws

Anyone who carries out plumbing work can be prosecuted if they commit an offence under the current Water Byelaws. This applies equally to professional plumbers and DIY amateurs. It is important to understand that householders also commit an offence if they 'use' a fitting that does not comply with the byelaws.

Any person – installer or user – who contravenes the Water Byelaws can be fined a substantial sum if convicted. Moreover, further fines may be levied on a daily basis if the offence continues after conviction. So it is essential to be aware of the Water Byelaws and to comply with them.

Nor is it simply enough to make sure that plumbing work is carried out correctly. The byelaws require that five days notice be given to the local water supplier before starting work on a variety of jobs. These include the installation of, or alteration to:

● A bidet
● A flushing cistern
● A hose union or a tap to which a hosepipe may be connected
● A fitting that could cause contamination of the water supply by backflow

Even threading a water supply pipe through a wall should be notified to the water company at least five days in advance. Failure to do so would be a contravention of the byelaws.

Over the years, the Water Byelaws have been modified and brought up to date, but they are not retrospective; installations that would have complied with the byelaws at the time of installation are not illegal simply because the rules have changed. However, any replacement fittings should meet the current regulations. There are exceptions to this rule, but they will be dealt with in the appropriate sections.

Building Regulations

Although the Building Regulations are mainly concerned with the construction and modification of the building itself, one or two sections relate to plumbing. Principal among these are the ventilation of kitchens and bathrooms, the installation of unvented systems, and drainage and sewage.

The regulations are somewhat difficult to interpret on their own, technical detail being given separately. Various guides are available, but your local building control officer or planning officer will be able to answer specific questions. These are also the people to whom you should apply if you intend carrying out any work that is covered by the regulations.

Gas Safety Regulations

Very simply, it is illegal for anyone to carry out any work in relation to a gas appliance or fitting who is not competent to do so. This includes installation, maintenance and repair. It also covers appliances that are fueled by stored LPG, whether it be in a tank or in a multiple-cylinder installation.

Although the techniques associated with gas fitting are very similar to those of water plumbing, the consequences of making an error are obviously very much more serious – it could result in loss of life. Such an error would result in the perpetrator receiving a heavy fine, or worse, on conviction. The only people considered competent to carry out gas work are registered by CORGI – the Council for the Registration of Gas Installers. Consequently, you should seek such an installer if you need any gas work carried out.

Work on gas appliances includes both the ventilation and flueing arrangements. Note that draughtproofing a room that contains an open-flued gas appliance may affect the air supply to that appliance. It is essential that adequate ventilation is maintained; the boiler manufacturer's manual should provide the necessary information. Also, adding an extractor fan in close proximity to a boiler with an open flue may cause the flue gases to be pulled back into the room, with potentially lethal consequences for the occupants. Such actions are covered by the regulations, even though the boiler itself may not have been touched.

IEE Wiring Regulations

Electricity is involved in many plumbing installations, and the appropriate regulations must be followed when carrying out any work involving that aspect of the job.

Although there are no legal restrictions on anyone carrying out their own electrical repairs and alterations (except in Scotland, where they fall under the Building Regulations), the local electricity supplier has the right to inspect and test any electrical work they think may be unsafe. Furthermore, they can refuse to supply power until any necessary remedial work is carried out to their satisfaction.

These regulations are regularly updated, but unlike plumbing, where additions normally do not affect the rest of the property, any additions to the wiring may mean making changes to the existing system. If you have any doubts about your competence to do a satisfactory job, call in a qualified electrician; electricity and water are uncomfortable bedfellows.

What are the Water Byelaws?

All water supply authorities have a statutory responsibility to make and enforce byelaws for the prevention of waste, undue consumption, misuse and contamination of water supplied by them. In fact, all water authorities throughout the UK operate to a standard set of byelaws (with only minor exceptions in special cases). To elaborate:

'Waste' means water that flows away unused – typically a dripping tap or a leaking pipe or fitting.

'Undue consumption' means water being used in excess of what is needed. For example, hand washing under a full running tap when a reduced flow would be adequate.

'Misuse' is water used for purposes other than those for which it is supplied. For example, a domestic supply being used for commercial purposes or, indeed, the use of a garden hose when it has not been paid for under the terms of supply.

'Contamination', of course, simply means the pollution of the supply by any means. This would include cross-connection between public and private supplies (i.e. mains and private borehole water cross-connected), and backflow into the mains through back-siphonage.

The danger of contamination is of most concern, although if the byelaws are followed, the danger will be non-existent. In fact, contamination is only likely to be a problem in the event of a failure of the mains supply. Under certain circumstances, and in the absence of backflow prevention devices, a drop in mains pressure could cause water to flow in the wrong direction, dragging contaminated water into the mains. For example, if a bath shower was being used for hair washing, and the handset was temporarily under water in the bath, then in the event of a mains failure, water from the bath could be siphoned back into the mains and contaminate the drinking water supply. What might reach the mains from a garden hose under similar circumstances does not bear contemplation. It is to prevent such eventualities that the Water Byelaws exist.

It is worth mentioning that the byelaws are not made directly for the protection of the consumer; they are there for the benefit of the supplier. Of course, the consumer does enjoy a constant supply of potable water, which the byelaws are designed to maintain.

The byelaws cover the installation of pipes and fittings, taps and valves, storage and flushing cisterns, sanitary and kitchen plumbing equipment, the types permitted, and how they are to be connected to the plumbing system. Fittings and materials accepted for use under the rules are listed in the *Water Fittings and Materials Directory*, which should be available in the reference section of your local library.

Although a fitting may be listed in the directory, it does not imply any degree of fitness for purpose. However, this can be verified by checking that the fitting is made to a British Standard or marked by some other recognised standards authority – European agencies, for example. (Bear in mind that taps and other fittings designed for Continental use may well carry a European mark, but they may not be suitable for use in a traditional UK low-pressure system.)

Chapter 3

Kitchens
Planning

Plumbing in the kitchen is focussed on the kitchen sink, the washing machine and the dishwasher. Other options for kitchen appliances are a water softener, water filter or waste disposal unit.

Designing a kitchen is less difficult than a bathroom from the plumbing point of view, because there are fewer restrictions on where appliances may be sited. However, although the hot and cold water pipes may not be difficult to move or place, the waste pipe to the drainage system should be kept as short as possible, which invariably means locating the sink and other appliances on, or close to, an outside wall.

The kitchen sink

The kitchen sink should be positioned so that it has work surfaces on both sides, and is either inset into the work surface or set on top of a cabinet base unit. The latter 'roll-top' sinks are designed to match the size of a standard base unit. Some have an upstand along the back to help throw water forward and make sealing against tiles easier.

Inset sinks are designed to sit comfortably within the fitted worktop area of standard base units, and are the most popular type. The taps for this type of sink may be mounted either on the rim of the sink or on the work surface itself.

It is common practice to place the sink under the kitchen window. This is usually convenient for running the waste pipe, but such placement is not essential provided the chosen site is well lit.

Sink shape

There is an enormous number of shapes and sizes of sink – from single-bowl inset without drainer to sinks with two main bowls, a small bowl (half bowl) in between and drainers at each side.

There are two important considerations when choosing a sink: the depth of bowl and the available space for the sink. A shallow bowl will not permit large pans to be washed easily, and it may be difficult to fit them under the tap(s). The space available, however, may restrict the size and shape that may be selected.

Not only are there many combinations of bowl, half bowl and drainer, but the bowls may also be round, square, rectangular or other shapes. The overall sink shape may be designed for a corner position, rather than in a run of worktop, and so on.

A point to note is the position on the sink of the tap hole(s), if any, because the sink must also be matched to the preferred type of tap. Sinks are available with a single hole for a mixer tap, two holes for pillar taps or twin mixer tap, or triple holes for mixer and drinking water taps. Alternatively, there may be no holes at all, so that the taps must be mounted on the wall or the worktop.

Sink materials

Stainless steel has been the most popular sink material for many years. It is hygienic, hardwearing, highly heat and chemical resistant, and is capable of being formed and fabricated into a wide variety of bowl configurations and sizes. High-gloss versions are prone to show scratch marks, but modern practice is to produce matt or satin finishes, which disguise any scratches.

Plastic sinks are also available, and have differing properties. Polycarbonate sinks, for example, are inexpensive, but may suffer unduly from cuts and scratches. They are not very heat resistant and may deform if a hot pan is put down on them. Because they are easily cut, they may lose their finish quickly and also become difficult to keep clean.

Sinks made from resin filled with silica are much tougher and more wear resistant. They come in a number of different colours. Others, made from resin filled with granite, are even tougher, and also come in a range of finishes and colours.

Enamelled steel sinks have been made for many years and now are available with vitreous enamel finishes of much improved quality, in a host of colours. Another well known type of sink is the ceramic or fireclay version, typified by the 'Belfast' sink of yesteryear and now back in fashion.

Taps

The popular choice for the kitchen sink tap is the mixer type with or without an additional hot spray/brush outlet. Almost invariably, the mixer tap will have a spout that swivels so that water can be directed to various parts of the bowl, or to other adjacent bowls. (Note that any mixer tap used where the cold water comes direct from the mains and hot water from storage must have a divided flow so that the water does not mix until it leaves the tap.) Alternatively, high-neck pillar taps may be used but, being fixed, they are much less flexible in use.

Kitchen taps are usually fitted with a sealing gasket between the tap and the sink or worktop, and nut and washer below. The swivelling spout on mixer taps is made leakproof by an O-ring between spout and base.

Waste outlets

Two types of waste outlet are commonly used in kitchen sinks. One is the standard chromium-plated type, which fits into a hole in the sink base and connects to the standard 40mm waste trap and pipe by means of a hand-tightened screw fitting.

The other type is the basket strainer waste, which uses a much larger hole in the sink (89mm) designed to accept a

Sink design varies considerably, as this deluxe design from Blanco shows. In addition to stainless steel, it is available in a very tough composite material.

waste disposal unit. This waste operates in two positions: in one, the waste is plugged in the normal way; in the other, the basket may be used to strain out larger debris, such as vegetable peelings, while allowing the water to drain away fairly freely. The vegetable waste may then be disposed of more easily.

Many suppliers package the sink with the correct waste pipes, overflows and traps needed for installation. Instructions should also be included, which will show that the trap must be fitted as the last outlet to the drain, as well as how to fit the various components together.

Removing an old sink

Fitting a new sink is a time consuming job, which means that the kitchen sink facilities will be out of action for a considerable time, unless the new sink is in a different location to the old one. If this is the case, the job could be planned so that the sink and all pipework is installed before having to turn off the water to the old sink and connect up to the new.

If the taps are fixed to the wall above the sink and the pipes come down from the ceiling, they can be left in place and operational until the rest of the installation is complete, leaving connection to the new pipes as the last job. However, this rarely happens, and the first job is to turn off the water, turn off the gate valve to the hot pipe near the cylinder, and drain down the hot and cold pipework. If the pipes are cut and stopped off with

endstops, the rest of the system can normally be reinstated by turning on the stoptap and gate valve. This keeps the bathroom facilities in operation but, unless the cold water to the bathroom taps comes directly from the mains and not from a cistern, no drinking water will be available. Kettles, pans and jugs may need to be employed for this; alternatively, a tap could be fitted temporarily on the cold pipe in the kitchen, after it has been disconnected from the sink. Jobs do overrun, and a lack of drinking water could become a problem.

Unless the connectors between the pipes and the tap tails can be reached and loosened easily, simply cut the pipes at a convenient place (water will be left in the pipes if they come up from the floor, so be prepared to mop it up). Any short pipe can easily be extended later.

Undo the waste trap, or cut it off, which should enable the sink to be lifted out after removing any clamps or fixing brackets. If the old sink is of the heavy fireclay/earthenware type, it will probably need two people to lift it out. Unless the waste is relatively modern, it will need to be replaced, probably in a different position to accommodate the different design of sink.

Basket strainer wastes for kitchen sinks. (Opella)

▶ SEE PAGE 70 FOR STEP-BY-STEP INSTRUCTIONS ON INSTALLING AN INSET KITCHEN SINK

A mock-up to show the Sanivite pumping unit for kitchens remote from the drains, or constructed in a basement.

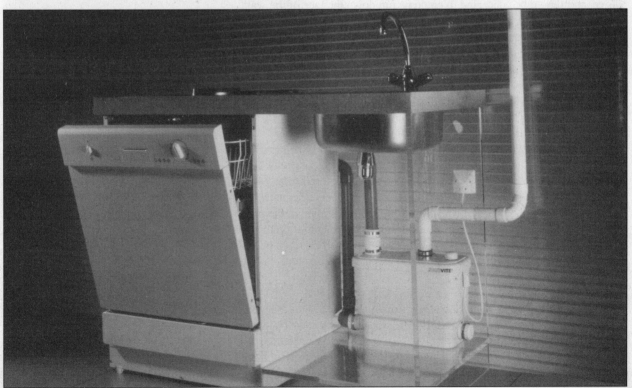

Installing a new sink

The technique for installing a new kitchen sink will vary, depending on the type of sink. A roll-top sink is simply laid onto the sink base and clipped in place. It should be an exact fit if both base and sink are to modern metric sizes. An inset sink will need a hole cutting in the worktop (or possibly an existing hole enlarging), after which it can be clipped in place. The step-by-step sequence shows the installation of a Leisure inset sink. When installing a sink, bear the following points in mind:

● Handle the work surface carefully after cutting the hole for an inset sink, as the amount of wood left on each side of the hole will be small and much weaker than the rest of the work surface.

● Fix taps and waste outlets to the sink before installing it. The waste and overflow will need mastic for bedding, unless rubber gaskets are supplied.

● If the sink is metal, it must be electrically bonded to the household earth, together with any metal pipes or wastes. A tag is often provided for this beneath the sink. Alternatively, the earth may be fastened to a clip holding the sink in place. Fastening the earth to the tap tail will not suffice, as the tap may be insulated from the sink by rubber or polythene gaskets.

Pipework

If hot and cold pipework is already installed below the worktop, connecting it to the new sink is simply a matter of extending it with appropriate pipe and fittings. Pipes under the worktop make the installation of washing machines and dishwashers much easier, too.

If there is only a cold pipe into the kitchen, a new pipe must be run from the nearest convenient hot supply. This may have to come down from the floor above, and should be concealed. It could be run down the face of the wall, through the worktop, and be boxed in, or the wall could be chased and the pipe buried under the plaster. In this case, any joints must be accessible, and copper pipe must be plastic-coated or wrapped in insulating tape to prevent corrosion.

Depending on the make of tap, there are two types of tap tail: the screwed connector, common on two-hole mixers; and long tap tails designed for compression or capillary connection, usually on high-pressure (mains-pressure) systems. The screwed connector uses a fibre washer to seal, which is easily lost when trying to make a connection at the back of the sink.

Since servicing valves should be fitted to the pipes close to the taps, but in an accessible position, it is good practice to fit the screwed connector and a short piece of pipe, plus the servicing valve, to the tap before fitting the sink in place. With plain tube tap tails, these normally extend about 25cm (10in) below the tap, and the servicing valve can form the connection to the pipe.

It is a good idea to assemble the sink and waste system before finally installing the sink. The position of the exit hole in the wall can then be fixed accurately and drilled before the sink is fastened down. Hire a hole cutter for this job; not only will the hole be the right size, but there will also be little making good to do.

Having cut the hole in the right place, it should not be difficult to pipe the waste from the trap through the wall. If there is a soil stack close by, the waste pipe can be connected to it, using a solvent-weld collar or convenient spare boss connection. Make sure that the fall is adequate. Alternatively, the pipe could be led to a convenient trapped gully linked to the drains.

TOOLS AND MATERIALS

☐ Tape measure
☐ Pencil
☐ Electric drill
☐ Wood bit
☐ Hole saw
☐ Jig saw or pad saw
☐ Screwdriver
☐ Adjustable spanner
☐ Inset sink unit
☐ Tap(s)
☐ Waste outlet
☐ Trap
☐ Copper or plastic supply pipe
☐ Compression or push-fit connectors
☐ Plastic waste pipe and connectors

Pipes, waste outlets, sink clips and fittings to complete the installation. Sometimes these come with the sink; in other cases, they will need buying separately.

1 After removing the old sink, it may be necessary to enlarge the aperture to accommodate the new one. To cut the hole, mark the outline (a template is often provided for this), drill a hole and cut the worktop with a jigsaw or padsaw.

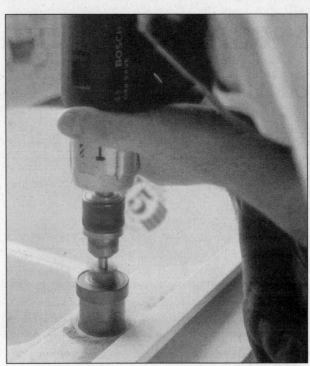

2 Holes may be provided in the rim of the sink for taps or, as in this case, it may be necessary to cut them. They should be made with a hole saw. This tool should also be used if the tap holes have to be cut in the worktop itself.

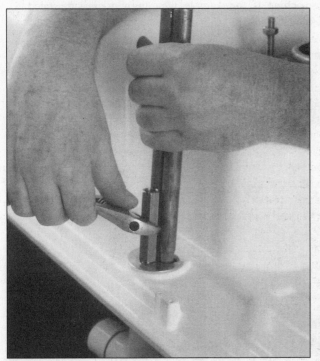

3 Fit the hot and cold water pipes for the mixer tap after fitting the sink waste and overflow. It will be much easier to attach them to the sink at this stage rather than after it has been installed in the worktop.

4 Set the sink in place in the worktop, and secure it with the fixing clips. Seal around the sink top, using a proprietary sealant. Finally, connect the supply pipes to the tap and the waste pipe to the trap and check for leaks.

Washing machines and dishwashers

Although some older washing machines can be filled by a pipe pushed onto the kitchen taps, most modern machines should be plumbed in. This removes the need to connect to the taps every time the machine is used and the extra supervision required. It also frees the sink for other uses while the washing machine is operating.

Most modern washing machines are of the hot-and-cold-fill type, only a minority being cold-fill only. However, the former will work as cold-fill machines, but will be much less economical. Because all the heat will be supplied by the internal heater, the cycle will be longer, and the machine will use more expensive peak-rate electricity, unless it can be programmed to operate at night and take advantage of cheap-rate tariffs. Dual-fill machines will not work if connected to the hot supply only. By contrast, most dishwashers are cold-fill only.

For both dishwashers and washing machines, the cold supply is usually taken directly from the mains supply, but this should be at a point beyond the draw-off to the kitchen sink. Alternatively, it may be taken from the cold cistern if the pressure is adequate. The hot water supply may be taken from most water heating systems, with the exception of a single point-of-use water heater.

Washing machines and dishwashers are designed to operate between set pressure limits. These are usually a minimum of 0.3 bar and a maximum of 10 bar. (If you have mains water pressure above 6 bar, you would be wise to fit a pressure limiting valve on the incoming cold main, immediately above the stopvalve, to limit the system pressure to a maximum of about 3 bar.)

The working pressure range of each machine will be specified in the manual. You should read this carefully and make sure you understand it before installation. For example, the instructions will indicate whether flow restricters are inserted in the cold and hot pipes to control water from the mains. With low-pressure mains water or cistern-fed supplies, these are normally removed.

If you intend locating the machine on, say, a first floor (perhaps in a bathroom) and feeding water from the cistern, the head of water from the top of the machine to the base of the cistern should be measured carefully to establish if sufficient pressure is available to operate the machine. If, for example, the minimum pressure stated in the handbook is 0.3 bar, the head must be at least 3m

Modern washing machines need a hot and cold fill, which means extending the pipework, as in this case, or tapping into existing pipework and fitting the appropriate servicing valves so that the water supply to the machine can be turned off when not required. The washing machine hoses simply screw onto the valves hand-tight.

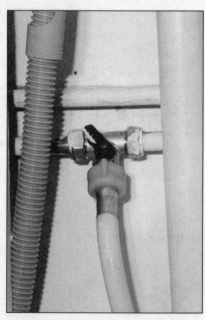

For the cold-fill dishwasher, the supply is teed from an existing cold water pipe, using a compression fitting that also incorporates the service valve.

(10ft) – 1m (3ft) head is about 0.1 bar. This may not be easy to achieve if the cistern is only just above the loft floor and the proposed site is on the floor below.

If the mains pressure is very low, it will pay to check the actual pressure with the water company, but as the minimum pressure at the outside stopvalve must be 1 bar, or above (with very few exceptions), low pressure at the machine is rarely a problem.

Plumbing-in

When installing a washing machine or dishwasher, two aspects need to be considered: the proximity of the water supply pipes, and the need for a suitable waste system. The latter is probably the more important of the two.

If the hot and cold water pipes run close to the position of the washing machine, it will be a relatively simple matter to connect the two together. Special connectors may be used that avoid the need to drain the pipes, and even turn off the water supplies. These clamp onto the pipe and cut a hole in it, an integral stopvalve preventing water loss. Subsequently, the stopvalve acts as an ON/OFF valve (water to washing machines and dishwashers should always be turned off when the machines are not in use). The flexible hoses of the machine connect directly to these fittings and need no tools for tightening – they should be hand-tight only.

Alternatively, the pipes can be drained and tee fittings inserted. Special fittings are sold specifically for these machines and incorporate stopvalves. If the machine is too far away from existing pipes for the flexible hoses to reach, compression tees or plastic push-fit fittings can be inserted so that pipes can be run to a convenient point for the machine. It is difficult to dry pipes well enough to use capillary fittings for such joints. Straight couplings, again incorporating stopvalves, are fitted to the ends of the pipes to accept the ¾in BSP hose unions.

Waste disposal

As with all wastes, the waste water from a washing machine (or dishwasher) must be discharged through a trap. The usual method is to hook the rubber waste pipe into the top of a vertical standpipe connected to a P-trap. This, in turn, should be connected to a waste pipe that runs through the wall to a gully.

Normally, the top of the standpipe should be 500-700mm (20-28in) above the floor, and there should be a gap around the top of the hose in the pipe. There should also be an air gap between the end of the hose and trap.

If the machine is located close to the sink, it may be possible the link the standpipe into a replacement trap system for the sink. Alternatively, if permitted by the machine makers, the hose may be pushed onto the nozzle

of a combined washing machine and sink trap, or onto the nozzle of a self-cutting waste connector fitted to the kitchen sink waste pipe.

It is most important that the manufacturer's instructions are followed when plumbing-in a washing machine or dishwasher. Otherwise, the machine may be damaged in use, and the warranty may be invalidated.

▶ **SEE PAGE 74 FOR STEP-BY-STEP INSTRUCTIONS ON INSTALLING A DISHWASHER**

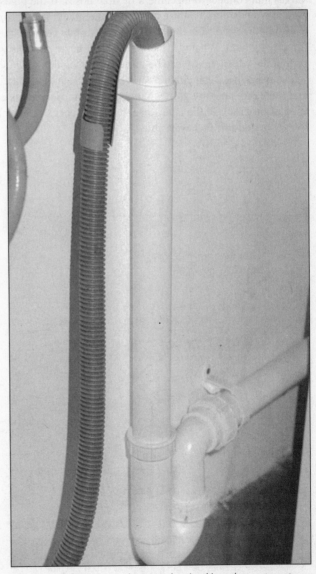

Waste water from the machine may be piped into the waste system of the sink unit via a special adaptor or, as here, into a separate waste pipe with trap. The pipe itself should be laid to a minimum fall of 1:40 to the soil stack or drain.

Plumbing-in a dishwasher

Whether you intend plumbing-in a dishwasher or a washing machine, the method is essentially the same, the only difference being the washing machine's need for a hot supply. However, this is arranged in exactly the same manner as the cold supply. This step-by-step sequence shows the installation of a dishwasher.

Plan the job carefully before you begin, working out exactly where you will take the supply pipes from and where you will run the waste. If there are no supply pipes near the machine's position, you will have to install new branch pipes after breaking into the existing pipework with compression or push-fit tees. These can then be capped with special washing machine/dishwasher valves that connect to machine's flexible hoses. If the pipes are close to the machine's position, you can break into them with self-cutting connectors, avoiding the need to drain the pipes, and simply connect the machine's hoses directly to them. Whatever method is used, make sure the valves are accessible so that the water supply can be turned off when the machine is not in use.

The waste hose can either be hooked into a standpipe incorporating a trap and linked to a nearby gully or soil stack, or it can be connected directly to a special sink trap. In the latter case, however, check the machine's instructions to ensure that this is permissible.

TOOLS AND MATERIALS

- ☐ Tape measure
- ☐ Pencil
- ☐ Electric drill
- ☐ Core drill
- ☐ Masonry bit
- ☐ Hacksaw
- ☐ Pipe cutter
- ☐ Half-round file
- ☐ Rat-tail file
- ☐ Adjustable spanners
- ☐ Screwdriver
- ☐ Spirit level
- ☐ Wire wool
- ☐ Small trowel
- ☐ 15mm copper or plastic pipe
- ☐ Compression or push-fit tee
- ☐ Washing machine/dishwasher valve
- ☐ Standpipe and trap kit
- ☐ 40mm waste pipe and fittings
- ☐ Pipe clips
- ☐ Ready-mixed mortar and plaster

1 Work out how you will run the waste pipe from the machine and where it will terminate. If the machine is installed in the kitchen, there may be a gully outside to which the pipe can be directed. Having drilled a suitable hole through the wall, in the correct position, assemble the pipe on the outside, running it at a minimum fall of 1:40 to the gully, where it should terminate below the level of the grille.

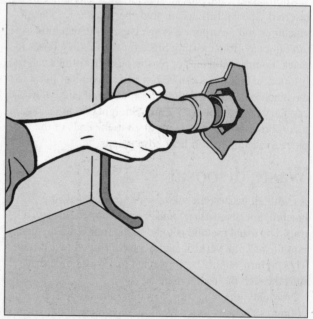

2 On the inside, run the waste pipe to the standpipe position, which should be behind or immediately beside the machine so that the waste hose can be hooked into it. Maintain the fall on the pipe, clipping it to the wall to prevent sagging and to hold it securely in place. With the pipe in position, any damage to the wall, caused when making the hole, can be made good with mortar or plaster.

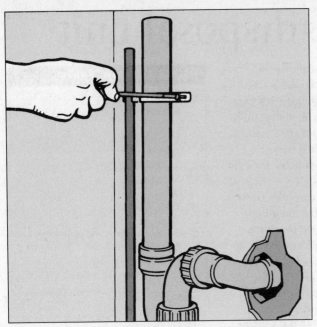

3 Offer up the standpipe and trap, marking the positions of the retaining clips. Make sure the standpipe is vertical with the aid of a spirit level, and that the trap is connected correctly to the waste pipe. Mark the positions of the retaining clips, and drill and plug the wall. Then fix the standpipe and trap permanently in place by screwing the clips to the wall. Check that the trap/waste pipe connection is tight.

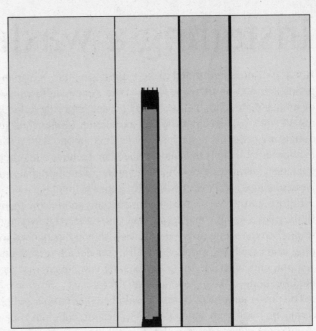

4 Run a length of 15mm pipe from the rising main, after the point where the supply is taken for the kitchen cold tap, clipping it securely to the wall. Prepare the end of the pipe for a proprietary washing machine/dishwasher valve. Slip the capnut over the end of the pipe, followed by the olive, then position the valve and tighten the nut. After making sure the valve is in the OFF position, restore the water supply.

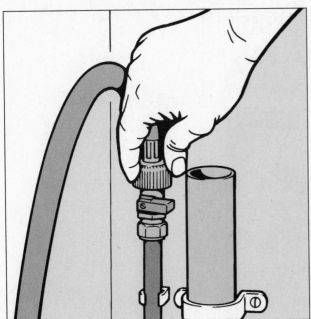

5 Check for any leaks at the joints of the new pipework, tightening compression fittings if necessary. Make sure that the sealing washer is correctly seated in the connector at the end of the machine's flexible inlet hose. Then screw the connector onto the valve's outlet. The connector should only be hand-tight, which is enough to make a watertight seal. Over-tightening can damage the connector.

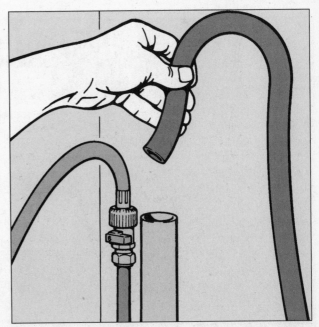

6 Hook the end of the waste hose into the top of the standpipe, making sure that there is space around it; don't attempt to seal the connection. Then position the machine, checking that it is level with a spirit level, and adjusting its feet if necessary. Finally, plug the machine into an electricity supply, turn on the water supply valve and test the machine in accordance with the manufacturer's instructions.

Installing a waste disposal unit

A waste disposal unit fitted to the kitchen sink will be capable of disposing of almost all food-based waste to the sewer system, lightening the load on the dustbin and reducing the risk of bad odours lingering in the kitchen. However, not all sinks will accept a waste disposal unit. Modern sinks with 90mm (3⅝in) outlets are generally suitable; an older sink, or one with a 38mm (1½in) outlet, may be suitable with an adaptor. The manufacturer's instructions will give guidance, but also check with the supplier of the unit that it is suitable for your particular sink, and that it will fit the space below.

Before starting work, read the instructions and follow them carefully. First, fit the inlet assembly and plug to the sink outlet, followed by the mounting ring. Then the waste disposal unit itself should be attached to the mounting ring, using the bolts supplied. Finally, connect a trap to the outlet of the waste disposal unit, and link this to the existing waste pipe, making such modifications to the pipework as are necessary.

The power supply to the unit should be taken from a switched fused connection unit with neon ON/OFF indicator, which may be run as a spur from a convenient socket outlet. Some units have their own ON/OFF switches, in which case, site the connection unit in an accessible location in the cupboard under the sink.

(*Note* If you have a septic tank sewage system, check that the tank itself is large enough to accept the substantially increased biological demand that a waste disposal unit will create. Additional biological treatment and/or more frequent emptying may be necessary.)

TOOLS AND MATERIALS

- ☐ Screwdrivers
- ☐ Wire cutters
- ☐ Sharp knife
- ☐ Electric drill
- ☐ Masonry bit
- ☐ Core drill (possibly)
- ☐ Wall plugs
- ☐ Screws
- ☐ Waste disposal unit
- ☐ P-trap
- ☐ 40mm waste pipe and connectors
- ☐ Pipe clips
- ☐ Fused connection unit
- ☐ 2.5mm² three-core cable

A waste disposal unit is a compact device that fits below the sink, providing a convenient means of disposing of a large amount of kitchen waste. Steel blades within the unit will grind waste material and mix it with water to form a slurry that can be flushed into the drains.

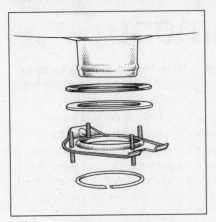

1 Disconnect the old waste pipe and discard the original sink waste outlet. Fit the new stainless steel sink outlet and suspension assembly.

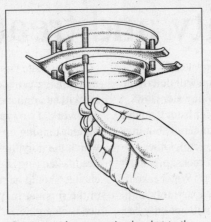

2 Secure the suspension bracket to the circular plates, using the screws provided. In this case, an Allen key is necessary to tighten them.

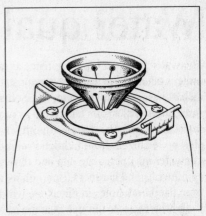

3 Fit the flexible anti-splash guard into the top of the machine's housing. Make sure that it is attached correctly according to the instructions.

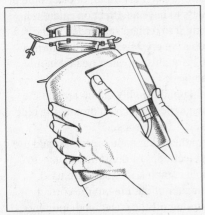

4 Lift the waste disposal unit into position, engaging the lug on one side with the suspension bracket attached to the sink outlet.

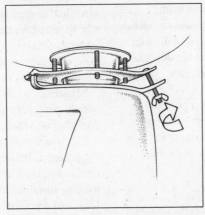

5 Rotate the unit until you can drop the wing nut into position and engage the remaining lug. Tighten the nut to secure the unit.

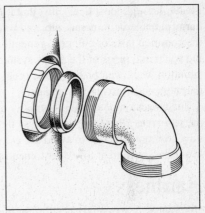

6 Fit the waste pipe bend supplied with the unit to the outlet at the side, using the compression fitting. Tightening the connector by hand will be sufficient.

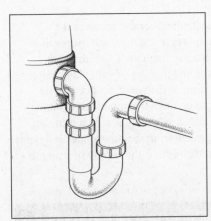

7 Connect the waste trap to the bend and waste pipe. The position of the hole in the wall may have to be altered to accommodate the new unit.

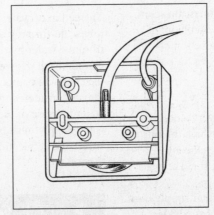

8 Locate the actuator in a convenient position, and connect it to the waste disposal unit in accordance with the manufacturer's instructions.

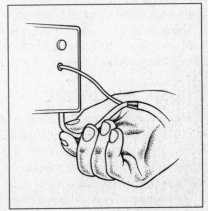

9 Directly wire the unit to a double-pole fused-spur switch, using three-core flexible cable. The connections must comply with IEE regulations.

Water quality and treatment

The water from our taps originates as rainwater, but the route it takes to the water treatment station will determine its hardness, mineral content, etc. Some rainwater flows straight into reservoirs and rivers as run-off from the land surface, and may be quite soft with few minerals, but may pick up fertilizers from farmland (nitrates, etc). Other rainwater may percolate into and through rocks, picking up minerals and hardness (lime) on its way. Water taken from deep bore holes in limestone will be extremely hard. If the water passes through peat areas, it will not only be very soft, but also acidic and may present a corrosion problem to copper piping.

Water from all these sources is treated in local treatment plants to ensure that it is potable, that is fit for human consumption. This does not mean that it tastes good (although most does), just that it is free from harmful bacteria, minerals, etc, and will remain so. Hence the common taste of chlorine, generally used to disinfect the water and pipes of the mains system. In the domestic situation, water can present three problems: taste, hardness and corrosion potential.

The corrosion potential is normally only a problem in the few areas where the water flows through peat, and it is now common practice to avoid the use of copper in these few areas, or to treat the water to neutralise the acidity.

Hardness

Hard water is apparently healthy for humans, but a major nuisance because of its tendency to block pipes, fur up kettles, coat heat exchanger pipes (making them very inefficient), and leave limescale stains and deposits around taps, on shower heads and on sanitaryware. In addition, hard water requires the use of much more soap to produce a lather, and also creates the limescale scum.

There are three possible remedies to the problem of hard water: phosphate dosing, magnetic/electronic conditioning, and softening.

Phosphate dosing

This is simply the controlled addition of very small quantities of food-grade polyphosphate, which inhibits the limescale from sticking to surfaces. It does this by assisting the calcium in the water to form small crystals, which remain suspended.

The addition of polyphosphate to the water supply does not make it any less potable. In fact, the chemical is widely used by the water companies in their treatment of water for public consumption.

A phosphate dosing unit can be simply teed into the rising main, using compression joints (or on the supply to individual appliances), whatever the angle of the pipework. Two types are available: those that need regular topping up with polyphosphate; and those in which the polyphosphate is contained in a cartridge that needs changing about once per year. The date when the change should be made may be provided on the unit itself, or the supplier may send a reminder that the cartridge needs changing.

Magnetic/electronic conditioning

The application of a strong magnetic field, or electronic or electrical charge appears to have an effect on calcium in the water, again causing it to remain suspended in the water as small non-adhesive crystals, rather than form a hard adhering scale. The quality of water treated in this manner remains unchanged.

Magnetic conditioning units simply clamp around the supply pipe. Electromagnetic versions fit around the pipe and plug into the nearest 13 amp socket.

Electronic units fit in the rising main pipework, and use the potential between electrodes of dissimilar metals to create the effect. Simple compression joints are used, making installation a matter of cutting out the correct length of pipe, after turning off the water, and draining down and fitting the unit in the gap. These units have a limited life, depending on how long it takes for the electrodes to dissolve.

Softening

The action of water softening literally removes the limescale-forming elements of calcium and magnesium from the water by replacing them with sodium from common salt. However, the process of softening changes the chemical composition of the water, so that it is no longer considered to be completely suitable as drinking water because of the added salt. This is why a drinking water supply must be taken from the mains inlet at a point before the connection that directs the supply of water to the softener.

▶ **SEE PAGE 80 FOR STEP-BY-STEP INSTRUCTIONS ON INSTALLING A WATER SOFTENER**

Tapworks automatic water softener installed under the kitchen worktop, where it is easily connected to the rising main.

Installing a water softener

Where possible, a water softener should be sited close to the rising main, allowing for any required hard water draw-off points. Water Byelaws require that one tap in the house remains unsoftened, and it is also recommended that the garden supply is not softened.

Water softeners have an effect on flow rate and pressure. Low or high pressure could lead to damage or non-operation. Daytime pressures should not exceed about 4.75 bar; if they do, a pressure reducing valve should be fitted. If the daytime pressure is below 1.7 bar, a pressure pump will be needed (but not connected directly to the mains). Flow rates must be over 1 litre (0.2 gallon) per minute for the water softener to be working at its design specification.

The water softener will be supplied with flexible hoses for connection to the plumbing system. However, if it is to be installed in an unvented system, the connections should be made with 22mm or 28mm copper pipe.

The softener requires a 24 volt, 50Hz power supply. The transformer must be plugged into a 240 volt outlet. The leads from the transformer are plugged into the appropriate connectors on the softener. After programming, the unit is tested by running water through, checking for leaks and that the cycle is working correctly.

The softened water will slowly replace the old hard water in the system over three or four days, so it will not be apparent immediately, except in those appliances that take water directly from the water softener.

The step-by-step sequence shown on the opposite page is based on the Ecowater water softeners.

TOOLS AND MATERIALS

- ☐ Pipe cutter
- ☐ Half-round file
- ☐ Rat-tail file
- ☐ Wire wool
- ☐ Adjustable spanners
- ☐ Tape measure
- ☐ Pencil
- ☐ Electric drill
- ☐ Core drill
- ☐ Water softener

Typical installation diagram, the softener being viewed from the rear.
A Check valve
B Pressure reducing valve
C Bypass valve
D Inlet valve
E Outlet valve

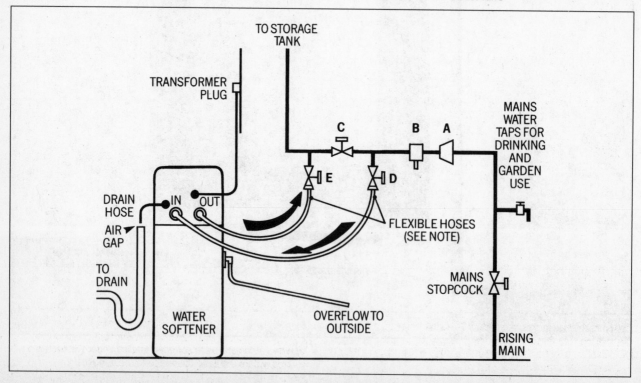

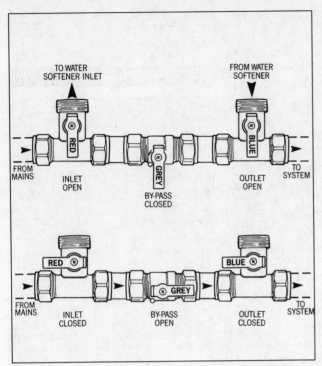

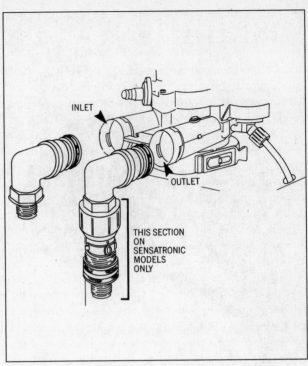

1 Cut the rising main and install the check valve. Next plumb the bypass, inlet and outlet valves so that the water supply can be turned on. Make sure that the valves allow the water to bypass the softener. A typical valve installation is shown.

2 Fit the inlet and outlet adaptors after fitting O-rings to the outer groove of each adaptor. Push the adaptors into the valve inlet, with the elbow pointing down. Models without an elbow meter use the same elbow for both ports.

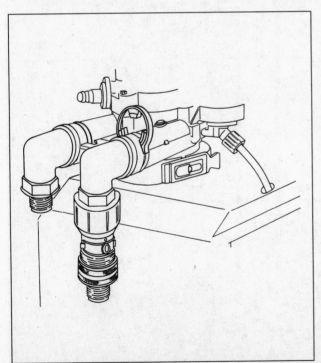

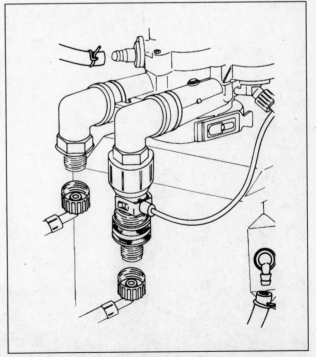

3 Snap the two large holding clips in place from the top down, making sure that they snap firmly into place. Tug on the adaptors to ensure that they are secure. Then install the meter sensor (Sensatronic models only).

4 Fit the inlet and outlet connections. The elbow connections fit on the adaptors, and the straight end is connected to the inlet or outlet valve as appropriate. Drain outlet and overflow connections must also be made as instructed.

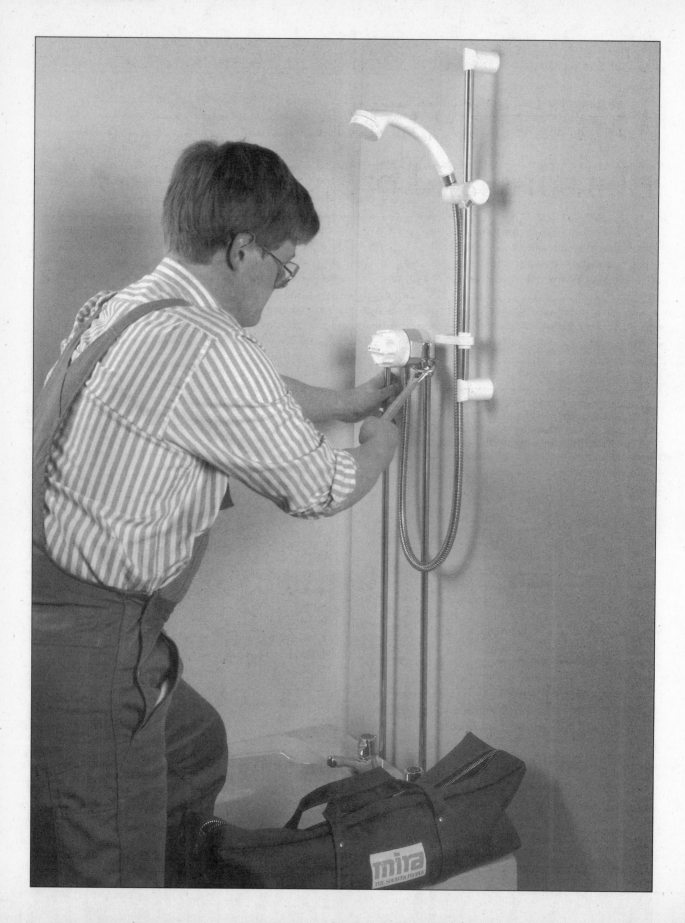

Chapter 4

Bathrooms
Planning and preparation

The bathroom is arguably the most important room in your home. Not only does it cater for personal hygiene, but it is also the one room in the house into which occupants can retreat behind a locked door for a few moments of personal privacy – a haven of warmth and indulgence. The fact that these functions are provided by the one room for people of perhaps widely differing tastes in style, colour and washing/bathing preferences, means that any changes to an existing bathroom, or the design of a new one, must be planned most thoroughly.

Unfortunately, the British bathroom was, and in many properties still is, small and cramped with little space for luxurious baths, showers, etc. However, pressure from consumers for more imaginative ideas, and for better performance from the facilities installed, has pushed manufacturers to create designs that not only fit into the smaller bathroom, but also provide improved style, convenience and luxury.

Most bathroom manufacturers provide products that have been designed to make the best use of the space available. These range from inset or tiny corner washbasins for the cloakroom to various sizes of basin and bath within a particular range. Corner baths can make better use of space than a conventional bath, while sit-up baths can double as shower bases. Some WCs have a shorter projection into the room than others.

There are even purpose-designed units that combine a bath and shower surround, with washbasin and WC to match. These will fit into a very small space indeed. Such combinations may make it possible to partition off a corner of a bedroom to provide full en-suite facilities where conventional products would be too large.

Changing the space

The refurbishment of a bathroom may allow a complete change of layout, plumbing permitting. The removal of an airing cupboard from the bathroom space – perhaps by moving the cylinder elsewhere, or by installing a combination boiler and making a cylinder totally redundant – will open up design possibilities simply not available within the original space.

If there is an adjacent, separate WC, removing the intervening wall can make more space available within the bathroom. However, with a large family and no other WC facilities in the house, the advantages of the extra space must be weighed against the reduced availability and lack of convenience.

Facilities and layout are interdependent, unless the bathroom space is large enough to accommodate all requirements. If it is not possible to fit everything into the one room, consideration should be given to placing some of the facilities, or indeed duplicate facilities, in another part of the home. For example, a shower and washbasin could be installed in a bedroom, or a WC in a cloakroom or under stairs, to free space in the bathroom, or to provide extra facilities to ease bathroom congestion at peak times. Such locations may need a waste drainage system that does not rely on gravity, and several automatic pumped systems are available to solve difficult location problems (see page 112).

Design considerations

A number of factors must be taken into account when contemplating the re-design of a bathroom. The position of a window will affect the positions of sanitaryware in the bathroom, and also the available wall space for a shower. If possible, locating the bath under the window should be avoided, because it severely restricts access to the window. The window itself will also be a source of cool draughts directly onto the bather.

The existing soil pipe position will limit the possible relocation of the WC. Indeed, it will probably be necessary to work the redesign around the original location of the WC.

Any underfloor drainage will be restricted by joist direction, but this can be overcome by having a step-up to the bath, creating a false floor with the joists running in a favourable direction. Problems with long runs of waste pipe (always more difficult to install discreetly than water pipes) may be overcome by using built-in units that also provide valuable storage space. This will be particularly useful if the airing cupboard has been removed.

If a shower is required in the bathroom, will there be room for a separate tray and enclosure, or must the shower be located over the bath? The separate shower enclosure or cubicle provides the better facility, and offers more choice of shape and scope for design. If there is no room available, an over-bath shower will provide the necessary function. Even if there is a shower elsewhere in the home, an over-bath shower may help in preventing washtime delays.

Style and colour

Although the style of a new bathroom suite will affect the budget – whether it be traditional, modern or nostalgic – it is unlikely to affect the layout, as most styles are available in sizes to fit all but the smallest of spaces. The colour of the suite, however, may be closely associated with the style. Many Victorian-style suites are only available in the traditional white, whereas other styles may offer a considerable choice of colours.

(*Note* The whole appearance of a bathroom, if fitted with a plain suite, can be changed dramatically simply by changing the colours of the curtains, towels, etc.)

Regardless of the form that the re-design takes, the sanitaryware must be positioned to allow easy connection to the soil, waste and water supply systems. More importantly, there must be enough 'activity space' around each piece of sanitaryware for it to be used and cleaned easily, although these spaces can overlap.

Planning the bathroom layout

Many bathroom manufacturers make planning easy by incorporating room grids and scale cutouts of individual items of sanitaryware in their catalogues. For layout purposes, any style will do, provided the sizes of the items chosen are the same as those of the intended suite.

All that needs to be done is to measure accurately the room size, and draw the shape onto the grid supplied, adding in doors (with opening direction), windows, radiators, etc, as necessary. Mark the existing plumbing points, such as water supplies, and waste and soil outlets.

If at all possible, use the existing soil outlet(s), as modifications may be difficult and costly. It is usually relatively easy to re-route water supply and waste pipes.

Then it is a matter of experimenting with the shapes to

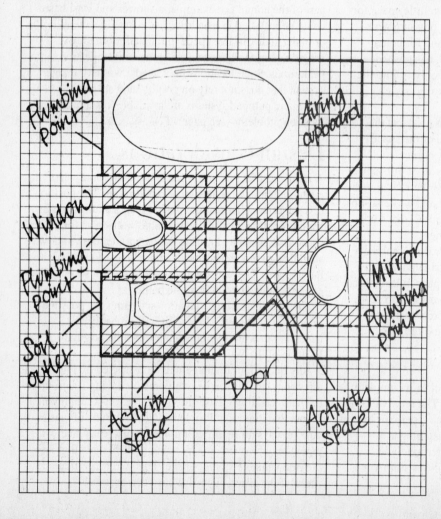

Most bathroom fitting manufacturers offer planning grids such as this in their catalogues, which allow you to arrange the positions of the fittings to make the most of the available space

find a layout that fits the space, suits the property and meets the family's needs. Once this has been accomplished, simply stick the shapes in position to provide a permanent record of the chosen design.

Installing sanitaryware

Having purchased the suite, including the taps and all other necessary pipe, fittings, wastes, etc, the next important decision is when to do the job. With another WC and a shower in the house, this may not be a problem. Otherwise, thought must be given to doing the job when the home is empty of other occupants, or to ensuring that alternative facilities are available.

Always bear in mind that, no matter how accurately you have estimated the time for installation, when the old suite has been removed, you may find that substantial making good is necessary before you can begin fitting the new suite. Also, plan to do the job on a day when you know the local plumbing supplier will be open. It is easy to miss a vital component at the planning stage, or to find that a component is not, as you thought, re-usable.

Draining down

Before attempting to drain the system, make sure that any immersion heater is switched off, and also the central heating. On a conventional system where the cistern is in the loft, or above the cylinder, and the cold supply is indirect, turn off valves controlling the pipes to the bathroom, if fitted, or tie up the float valve of the cistern. Then open the hot and cold bath taps. This leaves at least the kitchen supply in operation.

With a direct cold supply from the mains to the bathroom, turn off the main stopvalve. If the supply is mains-fed storage, simply turn off the main stopvalve and open the taps.

Servicing valves

If the new suite is being installed in the same position as the old suite, disruption may be minimised by installing one item at a time. This will leave the rest usable after the item being replaced has been isolated from the system.

This is easily managed if, after draining down, each pipe is fitted with a servicing valve close to the outlets, instead of just being stopped off. The rest of the system can be brought back into use while work continues on a fitting that has been isolated by turning off the valves.

As each piece is installed, it can be brought into use simply by turning on the appropriate valves. To work on the next piece, simply turn off the valves, replace the unit, re-connect to the services, and turn on the valves.

When the bathroom is being completely re-organised,

The Piccolo bathroom system, from Showerlux, allows for a separate bath and shower enclosure in the smallest of bathrooms.

such a method of working is not possible because of the necessary pipework alterations. However, if each pipe is stopped off (Speedfit endstops are ideal), the rest of the water system can be reinstated while work proceeds.

Removing the old suite

Care must be taken when dismantling if taps or fittings are to be re-used. Screws in walls will probably be corroded, making extraction difficult and the likelihood of breakage high. A hacksaw blade may have to be used to cut through supporting bolts or screws. It may also be necessary to cut the pipes rather than trying to release the fittings in situ. Cutting close to the fitting may help minimise remedial work on refitting.

Any damage to walls, etc, should be made good before installing any new items. This is particularly important for the floor beneath a new bath.

Installing a new bath

Probably the most difficult job in renovating a bathroom is removing the old bath. This can also be the most dangerous job if the bath is made of cast iron, which is a very heavy material. To lift such a bath safely really needs four men, but it is usually impossible to get that number of people into the bathroom, never mind into a position where they can lift the bath up and out. All too often, the only option is to break up the bath with a sledge hammer. It is essential to wear protective clothing, safety glasses and a hat for this job. Much damage and injury can be done by flying pieces of iron and chips of glazed enamel, so cover the bath with a piece of old carpet or similar. Also cover the window and any other items that may be damaged.

The only type of bath that needs no assembly is the cast iron variety; simply place it in position after fitting the waste trap and taps, and connect up to the waste and supply pipes. Other baths are supported on a frame and legs, the design of which varies from manufacturer to manufacturer. Therefore, it is important to follow the manufacturer's instructions. The step-by-step sequence shows the assembly of a typical acrylic bath.

Important considerations

It is important to ensure that the floor is firm enough to withstand the weight of the bath, water and occupant without sagging. If the feet are placed on timber floors between joists, a length of 75 x 50mm (3 x 2in) timber laid across the joists, under the feet, will improve stiffness. With thermoplastic floors, extra support to spread the load is needed, otherwise the feet will cause the floor material to 'creep' under the weight and pull the bath from the tiling.

When installing the bath, it makes sense to add servicing valves to the pipework supplying the taps, if they are not fitted already. Flexible connector pipes that incorporate servicing valves are available, making the connection and subsequent disconnection of bath taps in particular somewhat easier than with rigid copper pipe. (*Note* If pipes are to be run alongside the bath to another location, they should be run in front of the bath and behind the panel, not behind the bath against the wall.)

TOOLS AND MATERIALS

- [ ] Tape measure
- [ ] Pencil
- [ ] Screwdriver
- [ ] Adjustable spanners
- [ ] Pipe cutter
- [ ] Hacksaw
- [ ] Half-round and rat-tail files
- [ ] Wire wool
- [ ] Spirit level
- [ ] Taps
- [ ] Gate valves and supply pipes
- [ ] Waste outlet, trap and waste pipe
- [ ] Bath
- [ ] Bath panel, brackets and battens

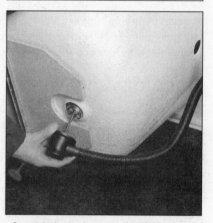

4 With the bath on its side, fit the waste and overflow assembly, including the pop-up mechanism if supplied, after removing the protective film.

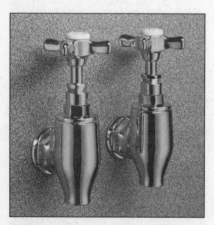

Globe taps, such as these from Pegler, are normally installed inside the bath, so double check valves must be fitted in the pipework to prevent back siphonage.

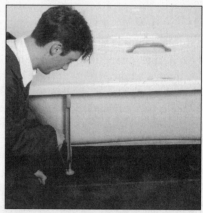

8 Place the bath in position and level it by adjusting the feet. Check also that it is at the right height. Connect the water and waste pipes.

1 Lay the bath face down on a clean, level surface, leaving the protective cover in position. Screw the two metal legs to the bath frame and the base.

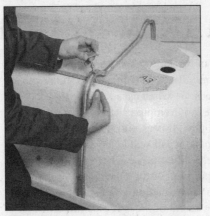

2 With the metal legs in position and firmly secured, bolt the four feet to them. Make sure the components of the feet are assembled correctly.

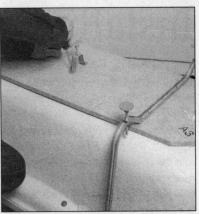

3 Screw the small leg and foot to the centre of the base. This is important to prevent the bottom of the bath from sagging in use.

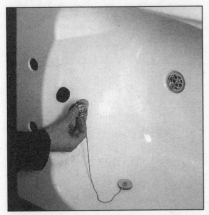

5 If a standard plug and chain assembly was supplied with the bath, screw the outlet to the overflow pipe. Make sure that it is secure.

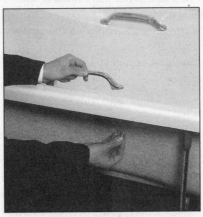

6 With the bath the right way up, fix the handgrips in position on each side. Make sure any protective gaskets are fitted beneath the grips.

7 Fit the taps in the holes provided. t is also a good idea to add the servicing valves at this point, together with connector pipes.

9 Drill and plug the walls, then screw wooden battens to them to support the bath panel. Affix the panel brackets to the battens.

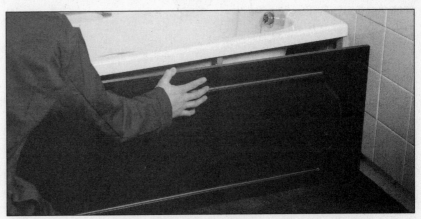

10 Restore the water supplies and check that there are no leaks from the new connections. Screw the catches to the bath panel to match the positions of the batten brackets. Offer up the panel to the brackets on the battens and push it home firmly to complete the job.

Installing a new WC and cistern

When removing a WC, a good quantity of bleach flushed through before starting makes the job much less unsavoury. If the WC links into a clay soil pipe, it will probably be cemented in place, in which case there is no alternative to very carefully breaking the WC exit pipe and chiselling out the piece remaining in the socket of the soil pipe. It is essential not to damage the soil pipe when doing this, as replacement or repair will be costly. Other joints may be of hemp and putty, which are generally much easier to remove, or the more modern connector, which simply pulls out of the pipe and off the WC.

When fitting a new WC in exactly the same position as an old one, check before fixing the pan to the floor that the height of the exit pipe matches that of the soil pipe. If necessary, raise the pedestal height by fixing a wooden plinth to the floor.

Because all sanitaryware shrinks considerably in the firing, each piece is unique and may not fit another exactly. As a result, a ceramic cistern lid may rock when placed on the cistern. However, a small roll of putty pressed onto the low spot will stop the rocking and harden in place.

The step-by-step installation sequence shows a close-coupled WC being installed. However, the procedure is essentially the same for other types, the only differences being in way that the cistern is supported and the need to install a flush pipe between the cistern and pan.

TOOLS AND MATERIALS

- ☐ Tape measure and pencil
- ☐ Screwdriver
- ☐ Pipe cutter
- ☐ Half-round and rat-tail files
- ☐ Wire wool
- ☐ Spirit level
- ☐ Electric drill and masonry bit
- ☐ Core drill
- ☐ WC, cistern and flushing mechanism
- ☐ Servicing valve and supply pipe
- ☐ Pipe connectors
- ☐ Pan/soil pipe connector
- ☐ Wall plugs
- ☐ Brass screws and caps

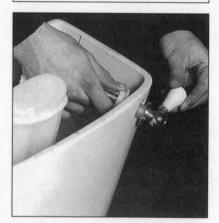

4 Next fit the flushing lever to the cistern, and connect up the linkage for the flushing mechanism in accordance with the manufacturer's instructions.

WC types

There are two types of WC: the siphonic, from which the waste is removed by suction, and the washdown, which is cleared only by the force of the flush water. The double-trap siphonic (top) is very quiet and efficient, and has full-bore trappage, which reduces the risk of blockage. Washdown pans may be flushing rim (bottom left) or rimless (bottom right).

8 Attach the cistern to the wall, using the screws provided. Don't forget to fit the plastic washers under the screw heads to protect the cistern.

1 The fittings for the cistern are normally supplied as a package with the WC. Unpack them and check that everything has been supplied.

2 Fit the siphon unit into the cistern, positioning it through the outlet at the bottom. Make sure the sealing washer is in place.

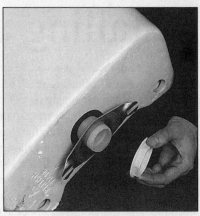

3 In the case of a close-coupled WC, the WC/cistern connecting plate is then fitted to the siphon. It is retained by a screw-on collar.

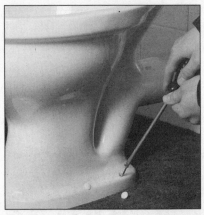

5 Fasten the WC to the floor with brass screws and caps. It may be appropriate to fit the pan-to-soil connector at this time and connect to the soil pipe.

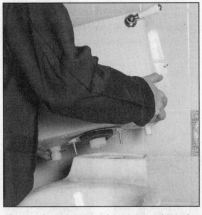

6 Sit the cistern on the pan, marking the wall for the fixing screw and overflow pipe positions. Drill and plug the screw holes; use a core drill for the pipe hole.

7 Fasten the cistern to the pan by fitting the wing nuts to the connecting bolts and tightening them. Take care not to over-tighten.

9 Fix the seat and lid assembly to the pan, passing the fixing bolts through the holes in the pan and securing them with wing nuts.

10 Having checked that the flushing mechanism is connected correctly, and operates as it should, place the lid on the cistern.

11 Note the servicing valve fitted to the cistern inlet ready to accept the water pipe. Connecting the pipe and turning on completes the job.

Installing a washbasin

Removing an old washbasin will be easier than removing a bath, and if you don't have a basin spanner to reach up behind to release the tap backnuts, simply cut through the supply pipes as close to the tap tails as possible. Then disconnect the trap from the waste pipe and unscrew the basin from the wall, and its pedestal (if fitted) from the floor.

The step-by-step photographs show the installation of a pedestal-mounted basin, but other types are available, too. Some basins can be attached directly to the wall using special threaded studs, while others rely on brackets for support. You can also buy inset basins for fitting into the top of vanity units in much the same manner as an inset kitchen sink.

You may have to re-route the supply and waste pipes to match the new basin, but this is best done after you have the basin in position. Obviously, if you are installing the basin in a new location, you will have to run in supply pipes and take the waste to a convenient hopper, gully or soil stack.

Keep the pipe runs as neat as possible, running them up inside the pedestal, where fitted. With a wall-mounted basin, the trap will be visible, so it is worth considering fitting a chrome-plated bottle trap, which will look less utilitarian than a standard plastic trap.

TOOLS AND MATERIALS

- ☐ Tape measure and pencil
- ☐ Screwdriver
- ☐ Pipe cutter
- ☐ Half-round and rat-tail files
- ☐ Wire wool
- ☐ Adjustable spanner
- ☐ Electric drill and masonry bit
- ☐ Core drill
- ☐ Washbasin
- ☐ Taps
- ☐ Plug and waste outlet
- ☐ Supply pipes and servicing valves
- ☐ Trap and waste pipe
- ☐ Pipe clips
- ☐ Screws and wall plugs

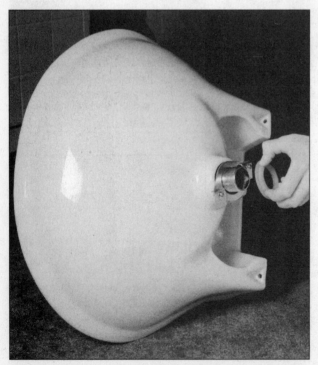

1 Insert the waste outlet through the hole at the bottom of the basin, making sure the sealing gasket is in place and correctly seated. Secure the outlet and the 'Kupla' fitting to the basin with the threaded collar provided.

2 Attach the taps to the basin, making sure the sealing washers are fitted over the tails first. If no sealing washers are provided, apply silicone sealant to the base of each tap. Then secure them with the back nuts.

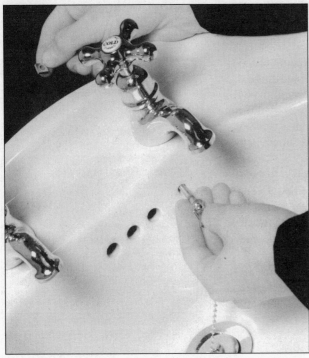

3 Make sure the taps sit at the correct angle, adjusting them if necessary. Then complete the basin by fitting the chain and plug. Insert the threaded portion through the hole provides and secure with a nut from behind.

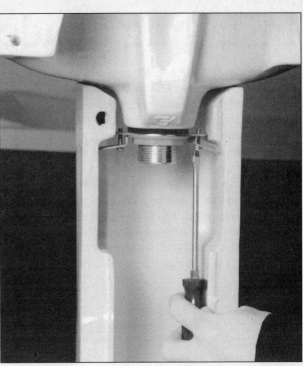

4 Stand the pedestal on a firm, level surface and carefully place the basin on top. Clamp the two together by tightening the screws of the 'Kupla' fitting. Make sure the screws are tightened by an equal amount.

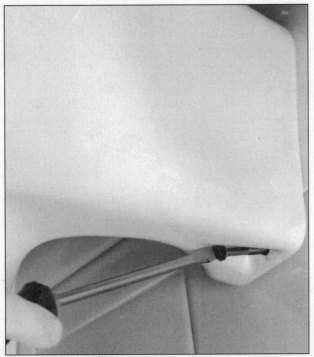

5 Offer up the basin and pedestal assembly to the wall, and mark the positions of the fixing screw holes on the wall. Drill and plug the holes, then replace the assembly and screw the basin to the wall.

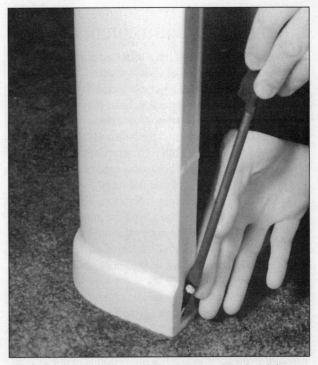

6 Screw the pedestal to the floor. Then complete the job by connecting up the water and waste pipework, running both neatly within the pedestal if possible and not forgetting the servicing valves.

Installing a bidet

The rules affecting the installation of a bidet are slightly more complicated than those applicable to a basin, because there are two kinds of bidet: the over-rim type, and the ascending-spray or through-rim type. The over-rim type fills the bidet from above, just like a washbasin, but the other type fills by directing the water around the rim, and usually provides a douche from an ascending spray set in the bottom of the bidet. The former type of bidet is shown in the step-by-step installation sequence.

There are specific requirements in the Water Byelaws that relate to the installation of bidets, and the local water company must be notified if you intend to fit one, regardless of its type. The plumbing requirements are set out below. The waste pipe from a bidet can be run to a hopper head in a two-pipe waste system; otherwise, it should be connected to the soil stack. If the bidet is on the ground floor, it can discharge into a nearby gully.

TOOLS AND MATERIALS

☐ Tape measure and pencil
☐ Screwdriver
☐ Pipe cutter
☐ Half-round and rat-tail files
☐ Wire wool
☐ Adjustable spanner
☐ Electric drill and masonry bit
☐ Core drill
☐ Bidet
☐ Monobloc tap
☐ Plug and waste outlet
☐ Supply pipes and servicing valves
☐ Trap and waste pipe
☐ 'Domex' screws
☐ Pipe clips
☐ Screws and wall plugs

Plumbing requirements

The two types of bidet have different plumbing requirements because of their designs:

● Because the spray is submerged in the washing water, the ascending-spray bidet may suffer from problems of back-siphonage, contaminating the mains water supply, if the Water Byelaws are not followed carefully. To ensure safe use, the hot and cold pipework to this type of bidet should be dedicated and not supply any other outlet (except the cold supply to a WC). The cold supply should be a separate pipe from the cold cistern, and the hot pipe should run from the pipe leading out of the top of the hot water cylinder, being fitted with a check valve and a dedicated vent pipe back to the cold water cistern. It must not feed any other appliance.

● With the over-rim type, provided the gap between the tap spout outlet and the rim overflow level is at least 25mm (1in) – a 'Class 1' protection – no other protection is required. Consequently, the supply pipes can be taken as branches from pipes supplying adjacent fittings.

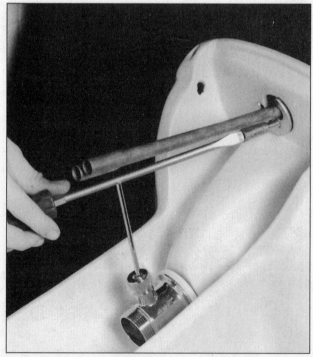

3 Fit the special backnut and tighten its screw to clamp the tap securely to the bidet. Make sure that the tap is positioned at the correct angle, adjusting it if necessary by slackening the backnut screw.

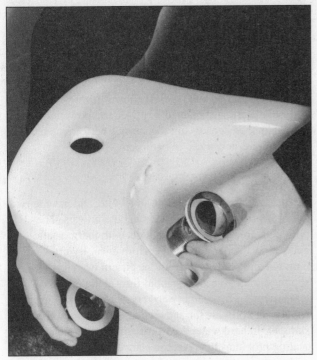

1 Slip the sealing gasket over the tail of the waste outlet and insert the outlet in the hole in the bottom of the bidet. Secure the outlet by screwing on the pop-up waste collar, again ensuring that the gasket is properly seated.

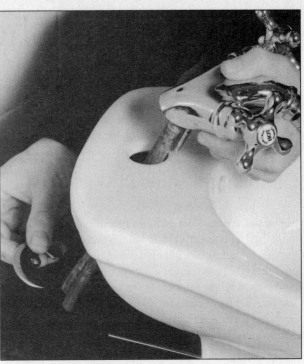

2 Insert the tails of the monobloc tap, with its pop-up waste control and swivelling nozzle, through the hole in the back of the bidet. Make sure that any sealing washers supplied are assembled correctly.

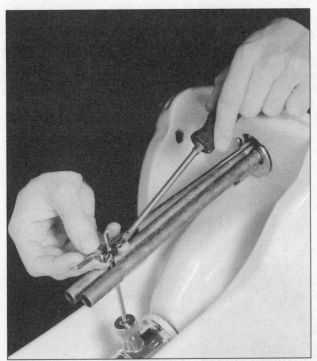

4 Connect the pop-up waste rod to the plunger on the tap. Then attach the rod to the lever projecting from the waste fitting. Check the operation of the pop-up waste, adjusting it if necessary, in accordance with the instructions.

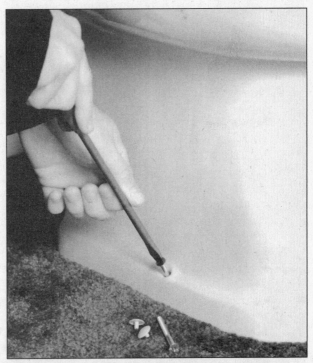

5 Position the bidet where required, and screw it to the floor with 'Domex' screws and caps. Connect the water supplies, using 15mm pipes. Then fit the trap and run the waste in 32mm plastic pipe.

Showers and showering

Showering is quicker, more hygienic and more economical of both water and energy than bathing. Also, taking a shower may well be physically easier than taking a bath for the elderly or disabled. A shower takes up much less room than a bath, and may be located almost anywhere in the property.

Choosing a shower

The modern shower can provide a vastly better performance than older versions that often produced no more than an uncontrolled dribble. Nowadays, all types of shower, including electric instantaneous showers, can provide good flow rates at controlled temperature. However, with the increase in the number of types of shower, and the various levels of performance they offer, choosing the correct shower needs careful thought.

Inevitably, choice is dictated by the limitations of the system. For example, there is little point in choosing a shower that is capable of dispensing large volumes of water if the plumbing system is unable to supply that volume of water.

There are three main types of shower from which to choose: electric instantaneous, mixer and power. All are available in designs to suit the various performance requirements and styles of bathroom.

Mixer showers

Mixers are suitable for almost any home, and have several advantages over electric instantaneous showers. They provide a greater flow, and models with thermostatic control give better all-round performance. By drawing both hot and cold water from the cistern or mains-fed supplies, they give a substantial flow at the selected temperature. They do not need connection to an electrical supply, and provide the same good performance winter or summer. In hard water areas, they are less prone to scaling problems than electric showers.

However, mixer showers depend on hot water being

Left *A shower need not be purely functional; it can be attractive, too, making it suitable for a bedroom as well as a bathroom.*

Facing page *Schematic view of a typical gravity-fed mixer valve system (not to scale), showing a flush-fitting valve and alternative take-offs from the hot water cylinder. (Illustration courtesy Triton plc)*

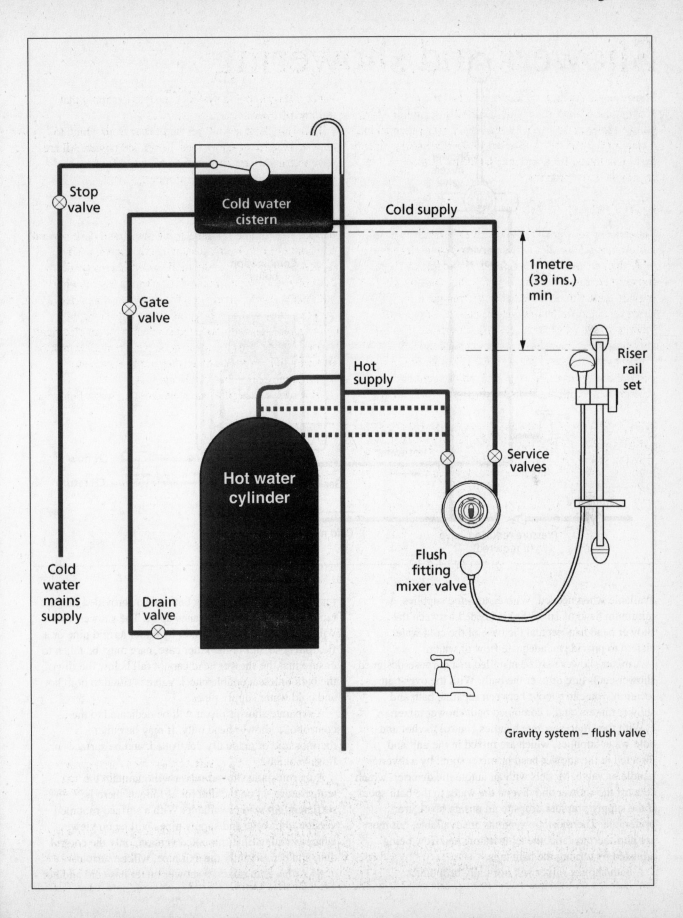

Stop valve

Cold water cistern

Cold supply

1metre (39 ins.) min

Gate valve

Hot supply

Riser rail set

Hot water cylinder

Service valves

Cold water mains supply

Drain valve

Flush fitting mixer valve

Gravity system – flush valve

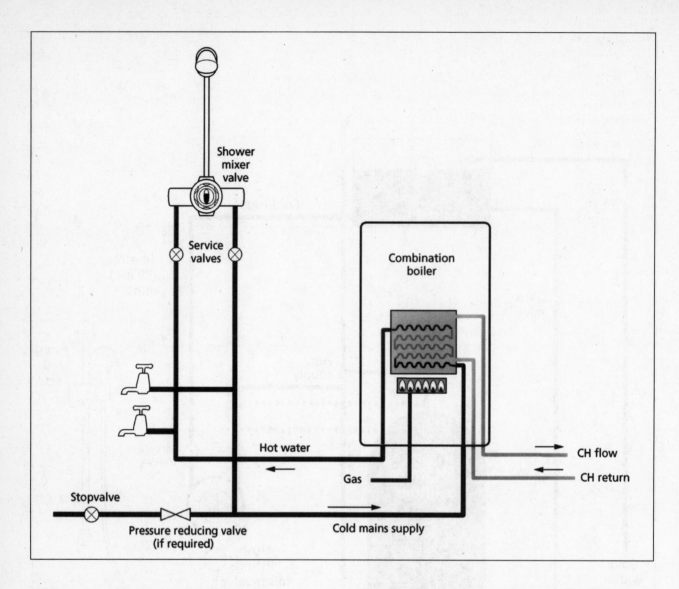

available when needed. With cistern-fed supplies, a minimum head of 1m (39in) is needed between the shower head handset and the base of the cold water cistern to provide an adequate flow of water.

A mixer shower may be installed in a purpose-designed shower enclosure or over the bath. With the over-bath location, you can choose between separate bath and shower mixers, and a combined bath/shower mixer.

With the latter, separate handles control the hot and cold water supplies, which are mixed in the unit and directed to the shower head or mixer spout by a diverter handle or valve. Models with an automatic diverter, which cuts off the shower and diverts the water to the bath spout if the supply pressure drops to an unsafe level, are preferable. Thermostatic versions are available, but most are non-thermostatic, the temperature and flow being adjusted by turning the bath taps.

A bath/shower mixer will normally be a direct replacement for an existing bath mixer, provided that the tap holes are the same distance apart. The shower head will be connected to the mixer by either a rigid pipe or a flexible hose, but in the latter case, care must be taken to ensure that the shower head cannot fall below the rim of the bath unless a double check valve is fitted to both hot and cold water supply pipes.

A separate shower mixer will be dedicated to the control of a shower head only. It may be either thermostatic or manually-controlled, and be surface- or flush-mounted.

A thermostatic shower mixer will maintain the temperature set on the dial for as long as there is sufficient hot water available. With a surface-mounted version, the valve and supply pipes will be on view, whereas with a flush-mounted version, only the control dial, and occasionally the exit pipe, will be visible.

As with a bath mixer, a shower mixer has cold and hot

Facing page *Schematic view of a typical mixer shower installation associated with a combination boiler. (Illustration courtesy Triton plc)*

Right *An over-bath shower must be fitted with check valves to prevent back-siphonage if the handset should fall into the bath water. This illustration shows the possible positions for those valves.*

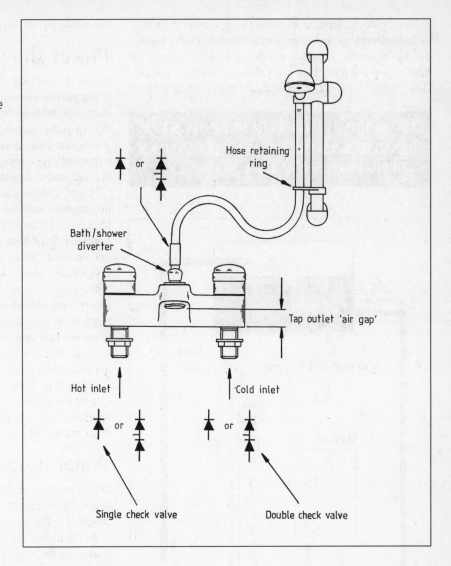

Hose retaining ring

Bath/shower diverter

Tap outlet 'air gap'

or

Hot inlet

Cold inlet

or

or

Single check valve

Double check valve

inlets connected to cold and hot supply pipes. With both thermostatic and manually-controlled mixers, it is preferable for the hot and cold supplies to be dedicated, being run as separate pipes from the cold cistern and hot cylinder. The hot supply should be the first draw-off from the pipe leading out of the top of the hot water cylinder. This minimises variations in flow and temperature when other outlets, either hot or cold, are turned on, particularly with manual types. However, even thermostatic versions benefit from the complete balancing and isolation of supplies. When installing a mixer valve above the bath with the bath tap supplies close by, it is still preferable to provide separate supplies to avoid fluctuations in temperature and flow.

Electric showers

These are the most versatile of all shower units, because they can be installed wherever there are mains water and electricity supplies. Electric showers provide instant hot water at any time, day or night, drawing water directly from the cold mains supply and heating it as it is used. They are particularly useful if stored hot water is not available, or if the heating is turned off for long periods.

It is essential to select an instantaneous electric shower with a large enough power rating. Because water is heated directly from the mains, the flow rate is controlled by the ability of the heater to raise the temperature to a comfortable showering level. Generally speaking, the more powerful the heater, the greater the flow.

▶ SEE PAGE 106 FOR STEP-BY-STEP INSTRUCTIONS ON INSTALLING A MIXER SHOWER

Many older instantaneous showers were rated at 6kW or less. However, during the winter months, mains water can be quite cold, so a shower rated at 8.5kW, or even higher, is preferable. This will provide a more satisfactory flow, water that is warm enough, and the possibility of having differing shower patterns.

▶ **SEE PAGE 108 FOR STEP-BY-STEP INSTRUCTIONS ON INSTALLING AN ELECTRIC SHOWER UNIT**

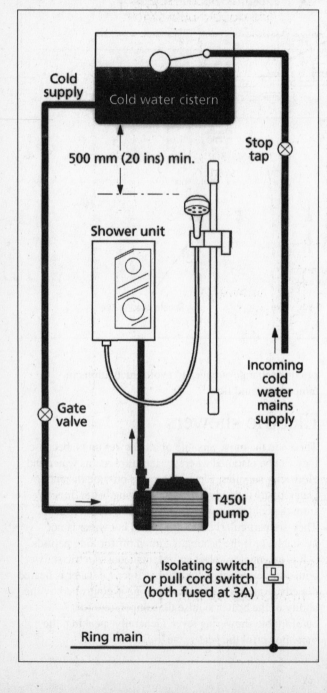

Power showers

Power showers are simply mixer showers that have the water pressure boosted by a pump, which automatically increases the flow from both hot and cold water supplies. With a pump-assisted shower, the pump may be positioned away from the mixer (ideally in the airing cupboard). However, with an all-in-one shower, the pump is contained within the control unit.

Power showers can provide the highest performance of all showers, with the additional benefit of precise temperature control for both comfort and safety. They are normally fitted with shower heads that can provide a number of different water patterns, ranging from an invigorating needle-jet or pulsating action to a soft 'champagne' foam. Additional body jets may also be incorporated for all-over performance. However, they use more water than other types of shower, so it is important to ensure that the cistern can fill as fast as it is emptied.

(*Note* Power showers may only be installed where both hot and cold water are supplied through a storage cistern. It is illegal to pump water directly from the mains supply, so a power shower may not be used where hot water is supplied from a combination boiler, multipoint or any other mains-fed system.)

Water usage

Different types of shower use different amounts of water, generally dependent on the pressure at which water is supplied to the shower head. The more water the shower uses, the higher the cost will be of heating it and, of course, of the water itself where it is metered. As a rule, power showers use the greatest amount of water, mixer showers the next and electric showers the least.

Shower location

The obvious place for adding a shower is over the bath, but a freestanding enclosure will give more flexibility of use. If the bedroom is large enough, a freestanding enclosure could be fitted in the corner of the room, together with a washbasin, to create an en-suite facility. Alternatively, unused space on the landing or under the stairs, or even a large walk-in cupboard or built-in wardrobe, could be considered as extra showering space.

Facing page *Schematic illustration of the layout for a typical electric shower system. (Illustration courtesy Triton plc)*

Left *Electric showers may be pumped if there is insufficient water pressure in the mains for a reasonable shower, but the supply must come from a storage cylinder. (Illustration courtesy Triton plc)*

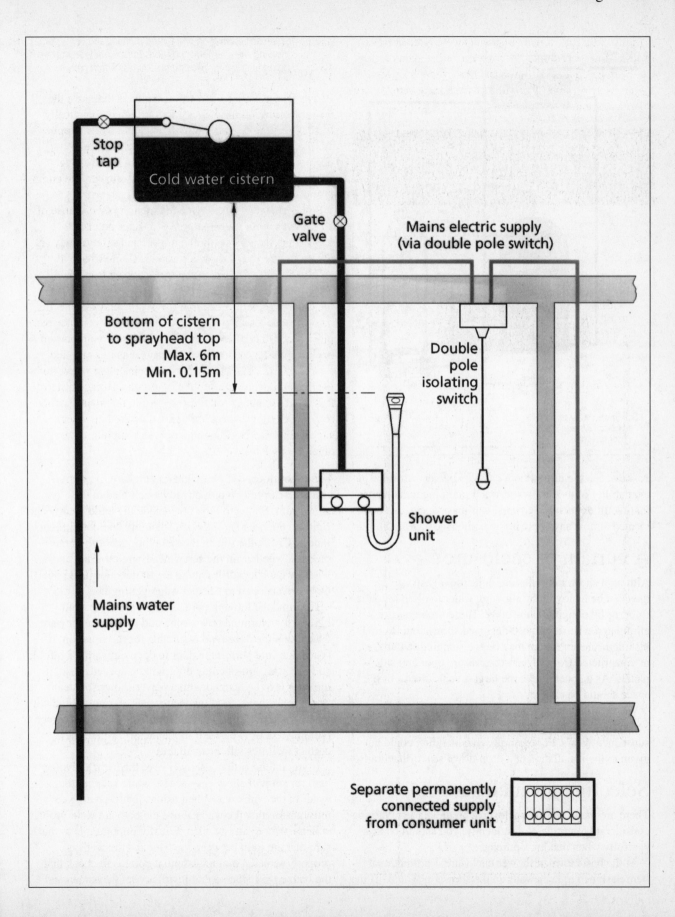

Stop
tap

Cold water cistern

Gate
valve

Mains electric supply
(via double pole switch)

Bottom of cistern
to sprayhead top
Max. 6m
Min. 0.15m

Double
pole
isolating
switch

Shower
unit

Mains water
supply

Separate permanently
connected supply
from consumer unit

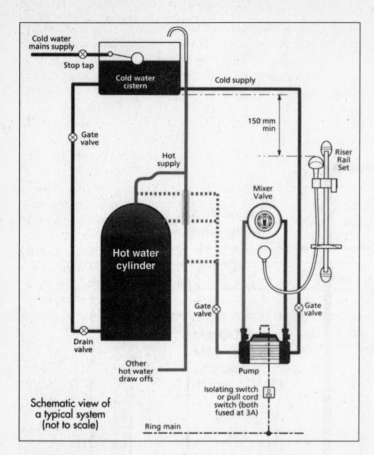

Schematic view of
a typical system
(not to scale)

*Schematic illustration of a typical pumped shower system,
showing the alternative positions for the hot water take-off
from the cylinder. (Illustration courtesy Triton plc)*

A shower in the utility room can also be very useful. The
availability of modern waste water pumping units means
that facilities such as showers, washbasins, etc, can be
located almost anywhere in the home (see page 112).

A curtain or enclosure?

Although shower curtains are quite inexpensive to fit,
they can be annoying by allowing water to drain onto the
floor, or by clinging to the body. These problems are
eliminated when a purpose-designed shower enclosure is
installed. The enclosure may be freestanding (a cubicle),
or constructed from a made-to-measure door and side
panels. As a general rule, the largest enclosure to fit the
space should be chosen.

While at the planning stage, some thought should also
be given to the way the needs of the family may change in
subsequent years. For example, consideration could be
given to the installation of a drop-down seat or handrails.

Selecting an enclosure

There are many shower enclosures on the market, varying
considerably in price. Consequently, you should choose
carefully when making a purchase.

At the basic level, a shower enclosure is a functional
item designed to keep water in the shower tray and off the
bathroom floor. Before making a purchase, if possible,
examine carefully a unit already assembled in the
showroom. Points to look for include the build quality and
rigidity; the door should open smoothly and not rattle or
judder. Check the finish, the smoothness of the frame
profiles, whether all the screw heads are covered, and
whether the cut profiles at the top of the door (and panel)
have been capped to prevent water getting in.

Examine the moving parts, such as pivot pins and
hinges, to determine how strong and well made they are.
Check that the door type is suitable for the situation. If
space does not permit the door to open outwards, a bifold,
sliding or inward-opening door will be needed. Also, if
the door is to be teamed with a power shower or steam
unit, it must have good magnetic seals all round. Find out
whether the door will be delivered fully assembled, since
building a door is best left to the factory, where the
correct facilities will be available.

If you intend fitting a shower over the bath, a pivoted
bath screen will allow easy access while keeping the
water in the bath area. When using a bath screen, you
must ensure that the walls above the bath are waterproof,
which normally means tiled. Equally important is to make
sure that the joint between the bath and the walls is
properly sealed. Another essential point is to check that
the bath edge is flat so that it will accept the screen and

can be sealed properly.

A power shower used over the bath, with only a short shower screen on one side, will splash water over the top and around the edges.

Shower screens and enclosures, including the doors, are often printed with designs that can complement the decor of the bathroom. Safety is an important requirement when choosing an enclosure. It should be fitted with toughened glass to BS6206:Class A, and carry a BSI Kitemark.

Selecting a tray

When considering which shower tray to buy, it is not just a matter of finding the correct size and colour or, indeed, price. The right tray will make installation easier and maintenance less traumatic if a blockage occurs.

Shower trays come in a variety of materials, as well as shapes and sizes. Most shower trays are made from acrylic sheet, in colours that match all the modern bathroom colours. A great advantage offered by acrylic sheet is that a tray may be made with an upstand around the edge, over which tiles can be fitted to provide a totally watertight seal. The alternatives to acrylic are ceramic (usually fireclay), stonecast resin (solid mineral-filled plastic), and pressed steel. Trays made from these materials are usually more expensive than those made from plastic sheet, but they can provide a very substantial base for a shower.

An important point with any tray is to ensure that, when installed, it permits easy access to the plumbing. It would be very expensive to have to remove the whole installation just because the waste trap became blocked.

Cheap acrylic trays may flex substantially, and can create sealing problems. Better quality acrylic trays have removable panels that allow access to the waste pipes. Some trays are supported on a adjustable legs so that height and level can be altered, making installation easier. So called 'stone' trays may be substantial and heavy, but they are prone to chipping.

The waste trap should be fitted with a removable top so that hairs, etc, may be removed simply by taking off the waste cover cap.

If the tray is to be used with a power shower, check that it will accept the volume of water delivered by this type of installation. Some power showers can dispense as much as 27 litres (6 gallons) per minute, and many more can output over 15 litres (3 gallons) per minute.

The rule is never to skimp on the tray; it is the foundation of a good enclosure.

Tray installation

Correct fitting of the tray is of paramount importance, as the functioning of the enclosure above it will be affected by poor installation. The tray must be supported correctly so that it will not be subjected to any undue strain from the weight of the enclosure, or the weight of the occupant when showering. This means that the floor under the tray must be firm. If stepping on the area causes the floor to flex, it should be reinforced.

If possible, the tray should be fitted to a floor and wall that have relaxed to their final positions. This is particularly important in newly-built properties, but may also be the case after refurbishment, as quite large amounts of movement can occur due to shrinkage and settlement. Such movement can only be accommodated successfully if a tiler tray, or tray with upstands, is used. This will take care of vertical movement, but if due attention is not paid to horizontal movement, particularly with a new wood floor, in extreme cases the upstand could pull the lower tiles from the wall, or at least break the grouting. Although a tiler tray may accommodate vertical movement, the enclosure may still have to be refitted if that movement is more than 3mm ($\frac{1}{8}$in).

Before laying the tray into position on the floor, fit the waste and trap, checking the alignment. When fitting an acrylic tray with adjustable legs, bolt the legs to the tray, set the tray in position, and level by adjusting the legs. Connect the waste pipe to the trap.

A stonecast or fireclay tray must be bedded on cement, making sure that there is good access to the plumbing underneath. It may be useful to set the tray on a raised plinth to allow room for the waste to be run underneath.

The next job is to tile the surround, or cover the walls with proprietary wallcovering (waterproof plywood-based panelling is available as an alternative to tiling and grouting for both bathrooms and kitchens). This tiling or wallcovering should extend beyond the enclosure. The panels and door (if fitted) must be fastened to the tiles, as a watertight seal cannot be guaranteed when tiling up to an existing panel.

Installing the enclosure

Before proceeding with the installation of the enclosure, it is essential that the manufacturer's instructions are read very carefully. No two manufacturers use quite the same methods of construction, and even different ranges produced by the same manufacturer may display considerable differences in their installation method. It is essential to check that the kit contains all the necessary parts, and also that any extra sections needed to

▶ **SEE PAGES 102 & 104 FOR STEP-BY-STEP INSTRUCTIONS ON MAKING SHOWER ENCLOSURES**

Assembling a shower enclosure

There is no universal method of installing a shower enclosure, as each manufacturer has unique frame profiles and designs. Therefore, the fitting instructions supplied must be followed precisely to ensure a satisfactory installation. However, the step-by-step installation sequence shown here provides a typical example of the necessary procedures and will give some idea of the work involved.

The end result should be an attractive, yet functional, facility that does not leak in use or from the door when opened.

1 Check that the tray is level side to side, front to back, and corner to corner with a spirit level. (All illustrations courtesy Daryl Industries Ltd)

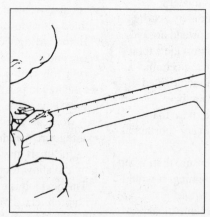

2 Mark the wall 6mm (¼in) in from the edge of the tray. Measure from the corner to this mark to ensure that it is within the door's adjustment range.

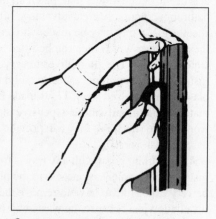

3 Next, remove the wall channel from the side panel. Then remove the corner post and the cover vinyl from the panel.

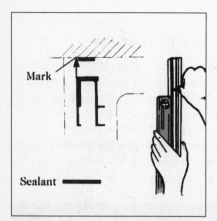

4 Hold the wall channel vertically on the wall in line with the mark made previously. Mark through the fixing holes onto the wall.

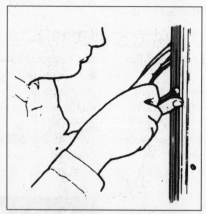

5 Drill and plug the holes. Then screw the channel to the wall. Apply silicone sealant between channel and wall before fully tightening the screws.

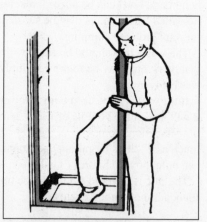

6 Slide the enclosure side panel into the wall channel. Seal under the panel where it meets the tray to ensure that there will be no leaks.

7 Replace the corner post on the end of the side panel, making sure that it is butted down onto the edge of the shower tray.

8 Adjust the width of the panel to the correct position for the door. Drill through access holes in wall channel and fix using self-tapping screws.

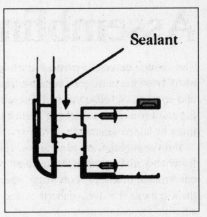

9 Offer up the door wall channel to the corner post so that the holes match up. Then apply silicone sealant between the sections.

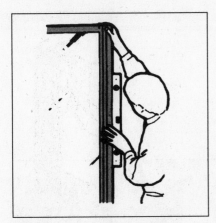

10 Make sure that the corner post is vertical, then drill pilot holes and screw the post into place. Fit caps to corner and wall channels.

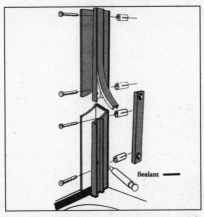

11 Rotate the door as necessary, depending on whether it is to be left or right opening. Then screw its wall channel to the wall, as before.

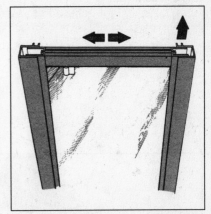

12 Fit the remaining channel onto the catch side of the door frame. Slide the hinge side of the door into the wall channel already on the wall.

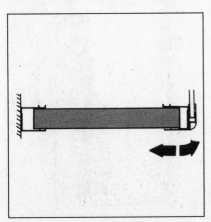

13 If fitting a door and side panel, ease the panel out until the door will slide into the wall channel. The corner post will then push onto the door.

14 Adjust the door so that it is centrally positioned within the channels. Screw door frame to channels and replace the cover vinyls.

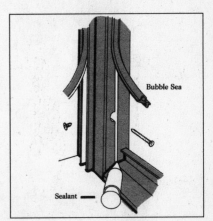

15 Apply silicone sealant all around the frame where it meets the wall and shower tray, and between the door frame and wall channels.

Assembling a shower cubicle

The shower cubicle is particularly useful for the provision of extra facilities away from the bathroom, because it needs no tiling or other waterproofing, and comes as a self-contained assembly. Some cubicles are even supplied with the shower unit as an integral part of the construction, although usually this must be added separately.

Shower cubicles are generally supplied in kit form for assembly on site. Invariably, they require the minimum of tools to put them together, and can be constructed in a very short time. Where no shower unit is supplied as part of the kit, a mixer valve, or thermostatic or electric control system will be suitable for installation.

The step-by-step sequence shows the assembly of a Leisure Fiji 2 cubicle, but the procedure will be similar for most other cubicles. Before beginning, it is important to check the contents of the kit to ensure that you have everything needed. Also read the instructions through carefully and make sure you understand them.

TOOLS AND MATERIALS
☐ Tape measure
☐ Screwdrivers
☐ Spanners
☐ Sharp knife
☐ Spirit level
☐ Cubicle kit

1 After unpacking and checking the components of the cubicle, the waste is fitted to the tray and a sealing strip applied to the top of the tray. A combined waste and trap is available that clears the floor. (All photographs courtesy Leisure)

2 Stand the tray close to the final position of the cubicle, but leaving room to work around it. After identifying the back and side panels, they can be loosely secured to the tray with the screws provided.

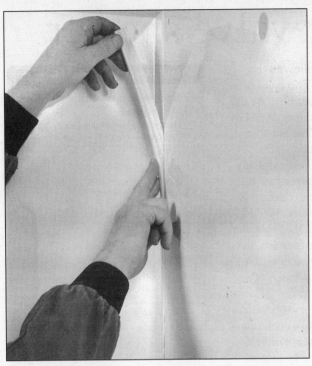

3 Lengths of flexible sealing strip are fitted between the walls to provide waterproof joints. The strips can simply be pressed into the gaps between the loosely-assembled panels with your fingers. Make sure they are seated correctly.

4 Lift the top frame into place, fitting it carefully to the inside of the side and back panels. Make sure it is located correctly, then secure the frame by driving screws into it from the sides and the back.

5 Check that the cubicle is square by taking diagonal measurements across the door opening. Both measurements should be the same; if not, adjust the panels until they are. Then tighten the screws in the sequence specified.

6 After moving the cubicle to its final position, the door can be fitted on its pivot pin (or a curtain hung). All that remains is to connect the waste pipe to the drain (or a pump unit), and fit the required shower unit with necessary pipework.

Installing a mixer valve shower

Mixer valve showers use the domestic hot and cold water supplies, mixing them together to provide a shower at the desired temperature. Two types of mixer valve are available: manual, where the temperature is controlled by the user; and thermostatic, where the temperature is controlled and maintained by a thermostatic device. Mixer valve showers provide a higher flow rate than electric instantaneous showers, but require a stored supply of hot water.

Although some units are claimed to operate well from a cold mains supply and a stored hot water supply, mixer showers generally work best when the supplies are 'balanced', that is come from similar sources. These can be the mains supply (unvented or mains pressure system), or stored water.

The mixer unit may be surface mounted or flush fitting. With the latter, the pipes may be visible or buried in the wall; with a flush-mounted version, the pipes are buried. Similarly, the shower head may be fixed (buried or visible), or on a flexible hose. The step-by-step sequence shows the installation of a surface-mounted mixer.

For gravity-fed systems, the top position of the shower head must be at least 1m (39in) below the bottom of the cold water cistern for effective operation of the shower. With both types, the pipes can enter from below, above or behind the mixer unit to suit the supply layout. Where a mixer unit is to be located over a bath, it it preferable to run separate supplies, rather than extending or tapping into the pipes to the bath taps.

Pipework

For stored water systems, the cold supply should be taken from the cold water cistern at a point below that of the draw-off to the hot supply cylinder. The hot supply should be taken from the top of the cylinder via an Essex flange or a Surrey flange (see page 120), or as some experts maintain, as the first draw-off from the supply from the cylinder to the rest of the hot system. Here, the pipe from the cylinder should incline at about 45 degrees, and the shower supply should be teed downwards. This allows air in the cylinder to vent away without being trapped in the water stream to the shower.

For mains-fed systems, the cold pipe to the shower may generally be teed from the most convenient cold water pipe, and the hot supply teed again as the first exit from the storage cylinder.

Mixer showers are also suitable for use with water heated by a combination boiler. However, care must be taken to ensure that the water supply pressure is adequate, that the unit is fed at nominally equal pressures, and that the flow is not significantly affected if other taps or appliances are operated elsewhere in the building. Combination boilers have limited flow rates.

The pipework should be installed before tiling, otherwise it must be surface mounted (preferably in stainless steel or chrome-plated copper). Unless the pipe runs are unusually long – in which case, it may be better to install an electric shower – 15mm pipework will suffice. As always, the rule is to flush out all pipework before connection to the mixer unit.

With flush-mounted valves, the pipes must be chased into the wall before tiling. As copper is susceptible to corrosion from mortar, it is preferable to use plastic pipes in a plastic pipe cover. This will eliminate joints under the tiling, except for those behind the fitting. Alternatively, fill the gaps around copper pipes with expanded polyurethane foam, trimming it flush before tiling.

TOOLS AND MATERIALS

- ☐ Tape measure and pencil
- ☐ Masking tape
- ☐ Electric drill, tile and masonry bits
- ☐ Core drill
- ☐ Pipe cutter
- ☐ Rat-tail file and wire wool
- ☐ Screwdriver
- ☐ Adjustable spanner
- ☐ Length of hose
- ☐ Spirit level
- ☐ Mixer shower unit
- ☐ 15mm pipe and connectors
- ☐ Check valves
- ☐ Pipe clips
- ☐ Screws and wall plugs

1 Offer up the mixer valve and riser rail to the wall, determining their positions. Mark the positions of the rail and valve support plate screw holes, then drill and plug them. Screw the rail and support plate in place. Then add the mixer valve.

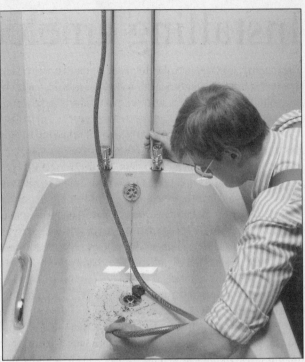

2 Run the hot and cold pipes up to position and flush out prior to attaching to the valve. Surface-mounted pipes should be either chromium-plated copper or stainless steel. They may be brought up from below or down from the ceiling.

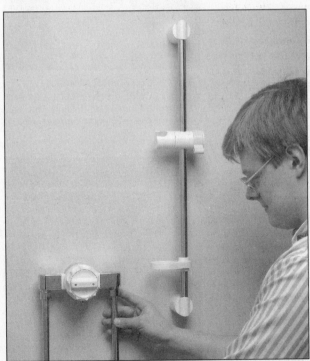

3 Attach the mixer valve to its support in accordance with the installation instructions. Then connect the hot and cold supply pipes to the correct mixer valve inlets. Tighten the retaining nuts carefully.

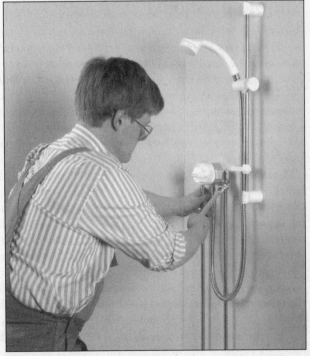

4 Screw the shower head onto the shower hose, and fit the hose onto the mixer valve. Check that all fittings are tight to ensure good seals. Then restore the water supplies at the gate valves, and test the installation.

Installing an electric shower

The electric shower, more correctly described as the instantaneous electric shower, is the most common shower type. It operates by passing water at a controlled rate from the mains over an immersion heater contained within a small cylinder.

It is also the easiest shower to plumb in, requiring only one 15mm pipe to be run from the mains supply, but is perhaps the most difficult from the electrics aspect. For this reason, a competent electrician should be employed to ensure that the electrical installation is correct and meets IEE Wiring Regulations.

A separate electric supply must be taken from the consumer unit to the shower, if there is a spare fuseway. If not, then either the consumer unit will have to be replaced with a larger one having more fuseways, or a separate MCB or switch fuse, together with suitable tails and connector block for subsequent connection by the local electricity company, must be installed. It is not possible to use a standard ring main circuit, where the maximum permitted load from any appliance is restricted to 3kW, for an appliance that may be rated at up to 9.5kW.

If an existing shower is to be replaced, care must still be taken to ensure that the correct cable size is in place, together with the appropriate size of fuse, or other protective device, to match the power of the new shower and its distance from the consumer unit. In general terms, and provided that the shower is not far from the consumer unit, a cable size of 6mm^2 is normally adequate. If not, 10mm^2 cable must be used. However, the installation must still be checked by a competent electrician to ensure that it complies with the regulations.

Simple plumbing

Once the electrical installation is in place and approved, the plumbing task, of running a supply from the mains to the shower unit, is relatively simple. The pipe should be fitted with an isolating valve for servicing purposes and terminate at the shower position with a compression or push-fit fitting, according to the manufacturer's instructions.

Maintained water supply pressure must be at least 0.8 bar for these appliances to function correctly. With substantially above 0.8 bar, the pipework may be run in 10mm microbore pipe connected to the 15mm inlet compression fitting.

Electric shower units must be installed on the finished wall, either onto tiles or proprietary wallboard designed for bathrooms and showers. The installation should be tested and the hose length checked to ensure that the handset cannot fall below the spill-over level of the bath or tray, which could lead to contamination. If this is possible, a hose retaining ring could be fitted or, better still, a double check valve could be installed in the water supply pipe, which should provide full protection.

Note The installation must be fully earthed, and all exposed metal parts (including pipes) within 3m (13ft) of the shower must be electrically bonded to earth, using 2.5mm^2 minimum cable size. An electric shower is a high-voltage appliance and must be installed safely by a competent person.

TOOLS AND MATERIALS

- ☐ Tape measure and pencil
- ☐ Masking tape
- ☐ Electric drill, tile and masonry bits
- ☐ Core drill
- ☐ Pipe cutter
- ☐ Rat-tail file and wire wool
- ☐ Screwdriver
- ☐ Adjustable spanner
- ☐ Wire cutters and strippers
- ☐ Spirit level
- ☐ Electric shower unit
- ☐ 15mm pipe and connectors
- ☐ Double-pole switch, cable and clips
- ☐ Pipe clips

4 Flush the supply pipe through with clean water to ensure that it is clear of debris before fitting the unit. This is a requirement of the Water Byelaws.

8 Run the electric cable into the unit and secure it with its clamp. Connect the cable to the unit in accordance with the instructions.

1 Set out masking tape on the shower wall to match the dimensions of the casing. Then mark the fixing screw, cable and pipe positions on the tape.

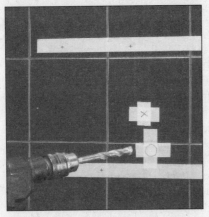

2 Drill all the holes. The tape not only provides clear drilling points, but it also prevents the drill bit from skidding across the surface of the tiles.

3 Having drilled all the holes, run in the water supply pipe and fit a compression elbow to its end. Plug the fixing screw holes.

5 Offer up the shower unit to the wall, aligning the fixing screw holes with the holes in the wall. Then screw the unit to the wall.

6 Connect the water supply pipe to the unit, using the compression fitting. Make sure that both capnuts are tight to ensure a watertight connection.

7 The shower unit is normally controlled by a ceiling-mounted double-pole switch. This should have both neon and ON/OFF power indicators.

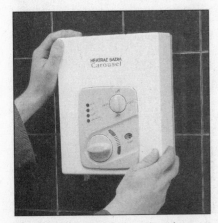

9 Place the cover on the unit and secure it, taking care to ensure that the control knobs connect with the internal drives.

10 Mark the position of the wall bar next to the shower unit, making sure that it is vertical. Drill and plug the holes, then screw it to the wall.

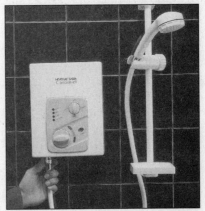

11 Connect the flexible hose to the shower unit's outlet and handset, locating the latter on the bar. Finally, test the unit.

Installing a packaged shower

Sometimes called a cabinet shower, the packaged shower consists of a thermostatic mixer shower combined with a low-voltage pump, all in the one cabinet. The low-voltage supply comes from an externally-located transformer, and provides a high degree of safety. The pump offers a maximum water flow rate of approximately 18 litres (4 gallons) per minute; double that of an instantaneous electric shower, and much better than many non-pumped, gravity-fed mixer showers.

A considerable advantage over electric showers is the simplicity of the electrical installation. All that is needed to install a packaged shower is a reasonably close power supply into which the transformer can be wired. The hot and cold water feeds should be taken directly from the hot water cylinder and cold water storage cistern respectively.

As with all pumped showers, a packaged shower must NOT be connected directly to the mains water supply.

TOOLS AND MATERIALS

- ☐ Tape measure and pencil
- ☐ Screwdriver
- ☐ Pipe cutter
- ☐ Half-round and rat-tail files
- ☐ Wire wool
- ☐ Adjustable spanner
- ☐ Electric drill
- ☐ Masonry and tile bits
- ☐ Hole saw
- ☐ Spirit level
- ☐ Supply pipes and servicing valves
- ☐ Push-fit pipe connectors
- ☐ Tank connector
- ☐ Pipe clips
- ☐ Screws and wall plugs
- ☐ Packaged shower unit

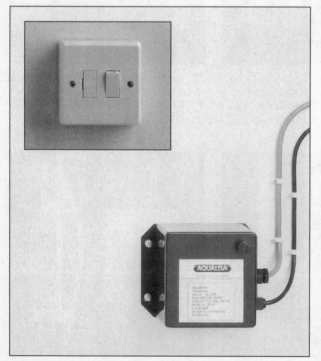

1 Install the transformer within 4m (13ft) of the shower unit, but outside the bathroom/shower; an airing cupboard is ideal. Wire it to a fused switch (inset) – again, outside the bathroom. (All photographs courtesy Aqualisa Products Ltd)

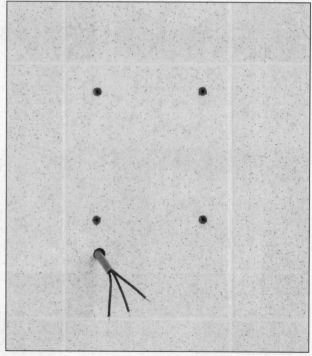

2 Decide on the position of the shower unit, and drill and plug fixing holes in the wall. Also, drill a hole for the low-voltage power cable. Run the cable through the wall, and fix the shower unit in place.

3 Tee into the existing gravity hot water system, preferably making it the first draw-off point after the cylinder. Fit a servicing valve to the branch pipe so that the circuit to the shower can be isolated if necessary.

4 Take the cold supply from the existing cold water cistern, at a point just below the draw-off for the rest of the hot water system (if the cold water supply fails, the hot water stops before the cold).

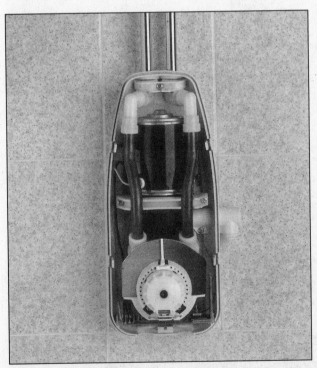

5 Run the pipes to the unit, either concealed or surface-mounted (use stainless steel for the visible pipe with push-fit connections to the other pipe). Make push-fit connections to the unit and complete the wiring.

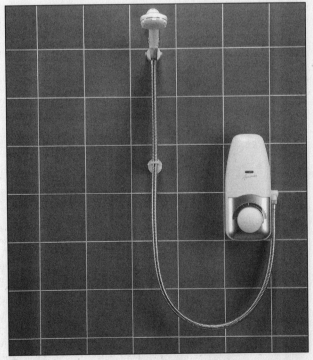

6 Fit the casing to the unit in accordance with the instructions. Drill and plug the wall, then fix the riser rail in position, making sure that it is vertical. Connect the hose to the unit and the shower head, and finally test.

Providing extra facilities

When attempting to add extra facilities to a property, it is usually the need for the waste pipes to have a fall towards the soil pipe or drain that presents a problem. However, by using a pumped system or macerator unit with smallbore (22 or 32mm) piping, every type of plumbing appliance – whether bath, shower, WC, bidet, dishwasher, washing machine or even the kitchen sink – may be located virtually anywhere in the property. This includes basements up to 3m (10ft) below the level of the main drainage system.

Where bathroom facilities are required, the unit sits behind the WC and, depending on the model, will accept waste from bidet, bath, washbasin and shower, as well as from the WC itself. For the kitchen, the appropriate model will accept the discharge from dishwasher and washing machine, as well as the sink.

All that is needed for these appliances, apart from cold and hot water supplies, is a supply of electricity, suitably fused, and the discharge pipework to the soil drainage system. The pipework can be laid to a minimum fall of 1:200 for 40m (130ft) horizontal discharge, or 1:40 for gravity discharge to any length beyond the vertical lift

point, provided the pipe size is large enough (32mm or larger). With some pipe systems, the first length of pipe on the vertical section can be as small as 22mm diameter, making a less obtrusive installation.

The pipe material must be either copper (using pulled or long-radius bends where necessary) or solvent-weld plastic, using two offset bends joined together to make 90 degree turns of sufficient radius. Push-fit waste systems are not suitable for pumped discharge.

The main installation factors are:
- There should be a 1:200 minimum fall on the horizontal pipes.
- Any vertical lift must come before the horizontal run.
- Any bends must be smooth and of long radius.

Three basic types of unit are available:
- A pump unit that attaches to the back spigot of the WC, which will also accept waste water from a washbasin, etc. This unit may also be used freestanding with the WC spigot hole plugged with a 100mm soil end cap.
- The pump actually built into the WC pan, which will also accept waste water from a washbasin, etc.

Saniflo macerator unit fitted on the spigot of a normal WC, and accepting the waste flow from the washbasin and shower, as well as the WC itself. This shows the versatility of such units.

● A freestanding pump unit that accepts waste water only from sinks, washing machines, etc.

Where possible, items with a low-level trap, such as a shower, should be piped to the unit separately from items having a high trap level, such as a washbasin, and also into opposite sides of the unit. Where this is not practical, pipe runs should be arranged so that the falls are steep enough to prevent backflow from high to low traps or, better still, a non-return valve should be fitted on the low-level pipework.

Special requirements

Water Byelaws state that a warning pipe from the cistern overflow should be visible so that action will be taken immediately to stop waste of water.

Because of the projection of the unit behind the WC, care must be taken on installation to ensure a correct fit. A close-coupled WC cistern may need 25-75mm (1-3in) of battening behind the cistern. Other WC designs have greater clearance to the wall and may need no battening, such as with a low-level, wall-hung cistern. With a concealed cistern, it may be necessary to fit a Multikwik extension to the WC spigot to allow both cistern and unit to be concealed.

This demonstrates what can be done with an understairs cupboard, in this case using the Sanichasse from Saniflo, which incorporates the macerator unit within the WC pan.

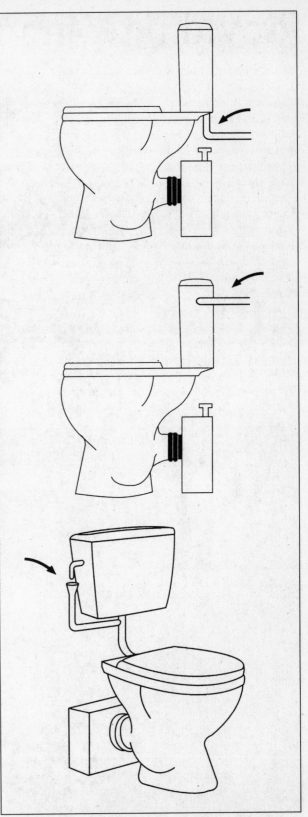

There are several routes for the cistern overflow pipe, including through the wall (top) or to a bath overflow manifold (centre). The set-up at bottom may be subject to building control regulations.

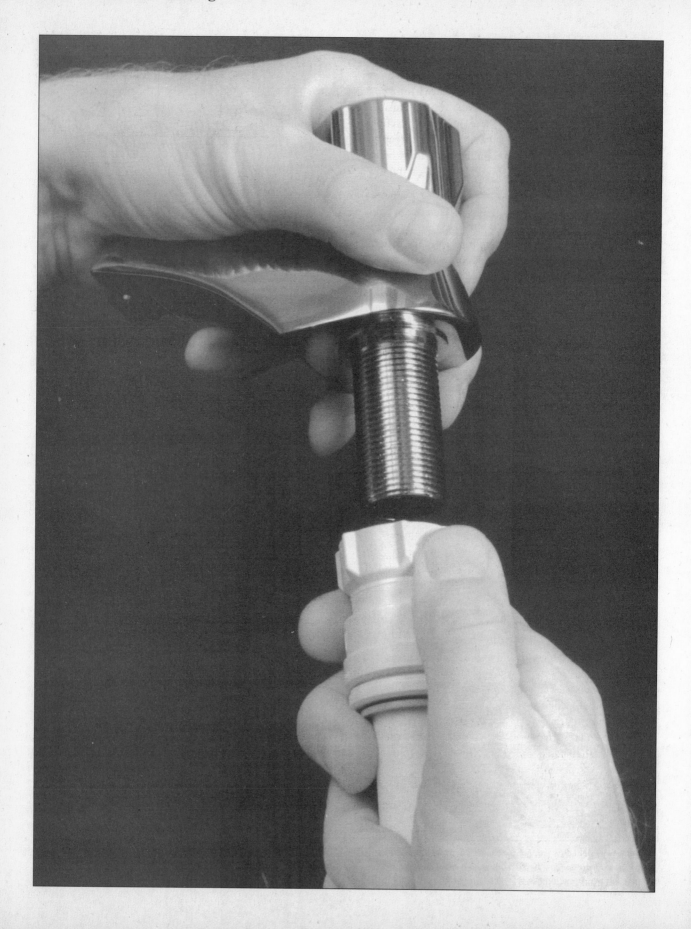

Chapter 5

General Plumbing
Taps and valves

Both taps and valves perform exactly the same function: they control the flow of water. The difference between them is that a valve is fitted in a pipe run, while a tap is fitted at the end of the pipe. Also, since valves are usually hidden, they are not normally given the decorative finish applied to taps which, invariably, are highly visible and often need to blend with a room's decor. A tap's decorative finish also prevents corrosion, which otherwise would occur on the bare brass from the effect of soaps and other chemicals in normal household use.

Although many different styles of tap are available, actually there are only a few types. Tap selection will depend on personal choice of style, in combination with the type required and the system in which it is to operate.

The latter is an important point, because continental taps, designed to operate on high-pressure systems, will not work well on the conventional low-pressure systems common in the UK, where the hot and cold supply is fed from a cistern (usually in the loft). Similarly, taps designed for low-pressure UK systems may not work effectively on mains-pressure or unvented systems. The type of tap is also important, particularly in the selection of mixer taps.

Pillar taps

Single taps, normally called pillar taps, are usually mounted one on each side of a washbasin, through purpose-made holes, or side-by-side on the bath. Each tap is secured by a backnut screwed onto the threaded portion, or tail, which fits through the hole. The threaded portion is normally ½in BSP for basins and sinks, and ¾in BSP for bath taps. (*Note* Kitchen sink taps are usually much taller than basin taps. This allows room for a bowl to be placed in the sink, underneath the taps.)

There are several types of pillar tap:
- The rising-spindle type, where the whole spindle moves as the tap is opened.
- The more common, non-rising spindle type, where the spindle lifts the washer assembly.
- The Supatap, no longer made, but for which replacement washers are still available.

Bib taps

At one time, the bib tap, which is screwed into a fixed wall plate elbow, was rarely used for anything other than garden water supplies. However, the development of in-wall pipe systems has led to outlet connections that are wall plate elbows, fixed so that they are flush with the wall (tiled) surface. These require a form of bib tap, which screws into the wall.

Mixer taps

There are several types of mixer tap, so called because they have two inlets and only one outlet. There are major differences between them, and the correct type must be selected to comply with the Water Byelaws.

Mixers may have divided flows, where the mixing only occurs at the end of the spout, or they may be designed so that the hot and cold water mixes in the body of the unit. If the hot and cold water are both supplied from a cold water cistern, either type may be used. However, if the cold water comes from the mains supply, and the hot water from the cold storage cistern, only the divided-flow type may be used.

If both hot and cold water come direct from the mains, either type of mixer may be used, but if the unit is a bath/shower mixer with a flexible hose, each supply pipe, or the shower hose, must be fitted with a double check valve to eliminate any possibility of back-siphonage. This assumes that an air gap exists between the tap outlet and the overflow level of the basin or bath. If not, double check valves must be fitted to the pipes from the mains.

The single-hole mixer usually has supply pipes of 12mm, or possibly 15mm, diameter and may, or may not, incorporate a connection for a pop-up waste. Three-hole mixers are similar to two-hole mixers, but have the extra hole for a pop-up waste.

Most two- and three-hole mixers have screwed BSP connections, but most single-hole mixers have plain (or plated) copper tube. Basin mixers have inlets at 102 or 210mm (4 or 8in) centres, and bath mixers at 181mm (7¼in) centres.

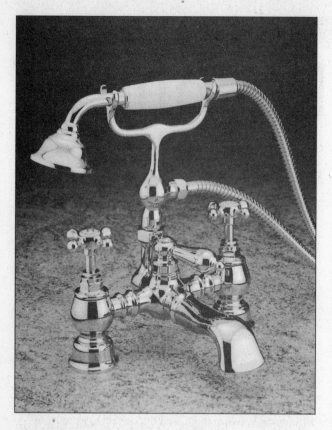

Two- and three-hole mixers have normal tap heads, or levers, on each supply to control the flow. Single-hole mixers may be operated by separate tap heads on each supply, or by the more modern single lever. The latter controls both the rate of flow and the mixing proportions of hot and cold water in the one action.

Improving appearance

An inexpensive way of improving the appearance of old taps is to use a conversion kit to replace the cross-head and easy-clean cover with a shroud head, which simply fits on to the top of the spindle. Sanitaryware manufacturers produce ceramic tap heads, colour matched to their suites, but these may only fit their own ranges of taps, so check before buying.

Fitting and replacing taps

Taps are fastened to sinks, baths, basins, etc, with washers and nuts. In the bathroom, they may have mastic between the body of the tap and the fitting instead of a washer or gasket, with a plastic or rubber washer underneath. Sink pillar taps are usually fitted with a plastic or rubber washer/gasket above and a 'top hat' washer underneath.

In either case, the nut must be tightened with a special basin spanner, designed to reach up behind the sink, basin or bath. This spanner is also used to turn the nut on the tap connector fitting. Alternatively, proprietary fittings, such as the Speedfit tap connector, may be used. These need only be tightened by hand.

With sink, bidet and basin mixer taps, the tap tails are often plain pipe. These allow push-fit fittings to be used as an alternative to the conventional compression or soldered fittings.

For ease of fitting, flexible connectors can be used, or lengths of plastic pipe. Alternatively, flexible corrugated copper tube connectors can be used, but these must be handled with care. Do not flex or bend them more than once, otherwise they may crack and leak.

To replace or fit new taps, the water supply to both taps must be turned off and the pipes drained. The old taps should be disconnected from the supply pipes (use an old towel to mop up the water that may spill from the broken joints). After removing the old taps, clean away any old mastic from around the tap holes, taking care not to damage the surface. Then fit the new taps, with their washers in the correct positions. Reconnect the pipes to the taps (adjusting the length if necessary), and restore the water supplies.

Above left *Two-hole bath/shower mixer.*

Left *High-neck kitchen pillar taps.*

Other types of valve

There are several types of valve other than taps:

● The stopvalve (or stopcock) is fitted on the rising main, and may incorporate an integral drain valve. The internal pattern of this valve is similar to a tap, with a spindle, jumper and washer. Unlike a tap, it usually has compression fittings at each end, and is marked with arrows to indicate the direction the flow of water must take through the fitting.

● A gate valve contains a 'gate', or paddle, which is raised or lowered by a spindle to control the flow, usually by turning a wheel handle. It should be kept in the fully open position (or just slightly closed to prevent jamming), and may be fitted either way round. Again, compression fittings are standard.

● A ball valve has a ball with a hole in it to control water flow. It needs only a quarter turn from fully open to fully closed, and is usually fitted with a lever handle that clearly shows whether the valve is open or shut. In the fully open position, this valve provides a full bore opening, which offers less resistance to flow than other types of valve.

● A servicing valve is a form of ball valve, but is usually turned on and off with a screwdriver in a slot, or a knob or short lever, such as is common on washing machine valves. Servicing valves should be fitted before all taps to allow easy maintenance, and to allow easy system balancing, which is important on mains-pressure and unvented systems.

All of these types of valve rarely give problems. Gland packing can fail in time, and can be replaced in the same manner as that of ordinary taps. Washers rarely fail.

With the exception of ball valves, all are prone to sticking in the open position, simply because they are not moved often enough. Stopvalves and gate valves should be turned off and on regularly, if only a few turns, to make sure they do not seize up. They should be left a quarter-turn closed after being opened fully. This won't affect flow, but should prevent sticking in the future.

If a valve does jam, a little penetrating oil or spray should be applied, repeatedly if necessary, until the valve is free. Undue force should not be used; it may damage the valve, or even the pipe.

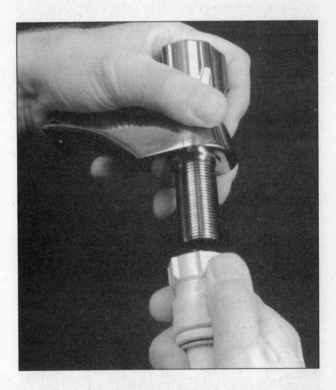

Above right *Quarter-turn ceramic disc mixer with pull-out spray.*

Centre right *The Speedfit tap connector allows for simple hand tightening to provide a leak-proof seal.*

Right *A ½in stopvalve showing typical signs of leakage from the gland around the shaft, together with a chrome-plated 15mm stopvalve for exposed positions.*

Installing a stopvalve

When extending an existing plumbing system, or installing a completely new system, it makes sense to fit valves of one form or another to the various pipe circuits so that they can be isolated for maintenance and repair work. These can be installed at the same time as the new pipework. However, many old plumbing systems may not have valves to control the various pipe circuits, which means that the entire system must be out of action while any work is carried out. This is far from satisfactory, so at the first opportunity you should remedy the situation.

In some cases, even the rising main may not have a stopvalve to shut off the water supply inside the house, which is something that should be attended to as a matter of urgency. Faced with a major leak, on a cold, wet night, the last thing you will want to do is scrabble about in the dark, looking for the cover of an underground valve that may be under water itself.

The step-by-step illustrations show the installation of a stopvalve and associated drain valve to an existing rising main, but the techniques can be used for installing any type of valve with compression joints. The job is quite straightforward, but it relies on the slight flexibility of the pipework to allow the valve assembly to be sprung into place between the cut ends. To make this as easy as possible, the pipe should be released from any clips in the immediate vicinity. Alternatively, a short length of pipe can be fitted to the valve, with a straight solder fitting slid over the end. This assembly should be fitted in the gap in the pipework, and the solder fitting slid over the joint between the two pipes and soldered in place.

TOOLS AND MATERIALS

☐ Tape measure
☐ Pencil
☐ Pipe cutter or hacksaw
☐ Half-round file
☐ Rat-tail file
☐ Wire wool
☐ Adjustable spanners
☐ Stopvalve
☐ Drain valve (possibly)
☐ Pipe (possibly)

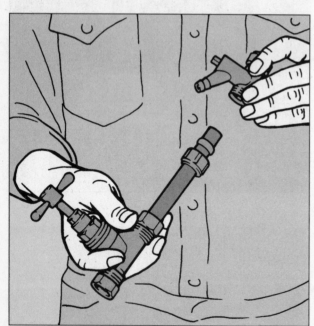

1 If the stopvalve is to control the rising main, the water supply should be turned off at the water authority's stoptap on the supply pipe to the property. Then you can assemble the stopvalve and a drain valve on a short length of pipe. The drain valve should be just above the stopvalve when installed, so that the system above can be easily and completely drained whenever necessary.

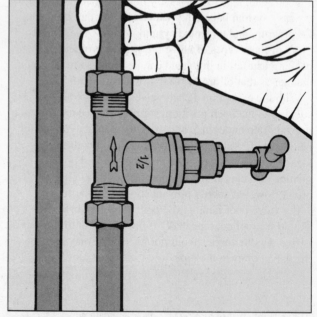

2 It is essential to fit a stopvalve the right way round, otherwise it will not be able to do its job properly. An arrow will be cast into the body of the valve to indicate the direction of the water flow through the valve. Another clue can be gained from the shape of the valve body below the handle: it tapers away in the direction of flow. A gate valve can be fitted either way round; it will accept flow in either direction.

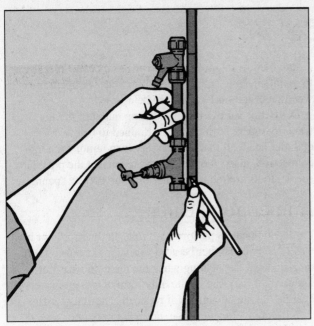

3 Make sure that the short pipe between the stopvalve and drain valve is inserted fully into each fitting and that the capnuts are tight. Then decide where on the rising main you want to fit the assembly and hold it alongside. Use a pencil to mark the amount of pipe that must be removed from the rising main. A shoulder formed on the body of each valve will give an indication of the cutting point.

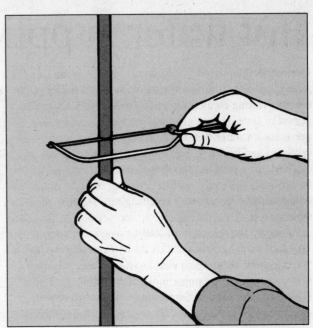

4 Make sure that your pencil marks are accurate. Then carefully cut through the rising main pipe at the points marked. You can use a junior hacksaw, as shown, a small pipe cutter or a ratcheting pipe cutter if you have one. With the last two, you are guaranteed a square end to the pipe, whereas if you use a saw, you must take extra care to cut it squarely. A piece of tape wrapped around the pipe will help.

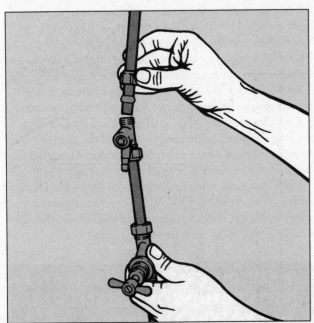

5 The most difficult part of the job is springing the stopvalve/drain valve assembly into the gap between the cut ends of the pipe. First slide the olives and capnuts of the fittings onto the ends of the pipe; you can tape them out of the way. Then slacken the capnuts holding the fittings to the short piece of pipe. With everything loose, and a bit of effort, you should be able to spring the valves into place.

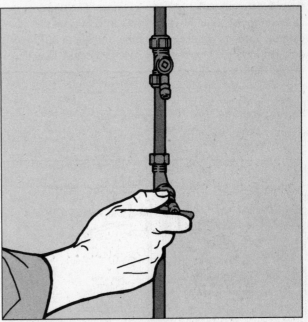

6 Tighten each capnut in turn, setting the positions of the valves as required; the stopvalve handle should face away from the wall so that you can turn it off easily without skinning your knuckles on the wall. With everything tight, and both valves closed, restore the water supply and check the joints for leaks. If all is well, open up the stopvalve to supply water to the rest of the system.

Hot water supplies

In most cases, domestic hot water is supplied from a storage cylinder, the water being heated by a boiler or electric heating elements in the cylinder itself. Over a period of time, the cylinder may no longer meet your needs for a variety of reasons: it may have become corroded and begun to leak; it may have insufficient capacity for a growing family's needs; you may prefer to fit a modern, properly insulated version in place of an unlagged type; or you may be changing the hot water system from direct to indirect, or vice versa.

Whatever the reason for installing a new cylinder, it may be a useful exercise at this time to assess if the hot water system performs as well as you require. If it does not, you can take the opportunity of installing a cylinder system of improved performance (mains pressure, for example), and remove the cold water cistern from the loft.

The Surrey flange

A device designed to draw off hot water from a relatively air-free position, just below the top of the hot water cylinder, is known as the Surrey flange. Hot water supply to the shower, or for any other critical use, comes via a centrally-mounted draw-off tube, which is offset to one side of the main outlet from the cylinder. The flange allows trapped air and water vapour to vent from the cylinder through the expansion pipe, and not to be dragged into the shower supply, where it could disrupt thermostatic control, etc.

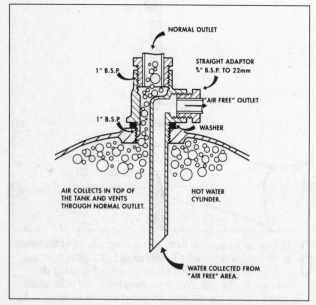

The Surrey flange prevents disruption to the temperature and flow of hot water supplies to showers.

Another advantage is that the position of the inlet helps to maintain flow, and hence shower water temperature when other hot outlets are also being used.

The flange simply fits into the top outlet of the hot water cylinder. With the water drained to below the cylinder head, all that is necessary is to remove the top connection, insert the flange, and reconnect the pipe. No special tools are required other than the correct spanners.

Immersion heaters

Immersion heaters perform two roles in the supply of hot water. They can either be used as a supplementary source of cylinder water heating when the main boiler is not required, or they can be the only form of storage water heating, taking advantage of reduced electricity tariffs.

In the supplementary role, normally only one immersion heater (either single- or dual-element) is fitted to the cylinder. When used as the primary source of heat, however, two or more horizontal immersion heaters are installed. The lower element is normally wired up to operate during off-peak tariff times, while the upper heater is wired for peak-rate top-up duties during the day.

Long, single or dual elements may be mounted to the top of the cylinder, while short, single elements are likely to be mounted horizontally near the base. Since only the water above the lowest point of the element will be heated, it is important that any heater projecting down from the top is of the correct length to heat the whole cylinder. Also, it must not foul either the heating coil or any corrosion-inhibiting anode fitted within the cylinder.

Dual elements may also be wired for off-peak heating, the long element for off-peak tariffs, and the shorter element for peak daytime use. Separate wires from the control switches should be used for each heater.

Each immersion heater must be fitted with a thermostat, which should be set at 60°C. This temperature provides water that is hot enough for domestic use without the danger of excessive scale formation in hard water areas.

▶ **SEE PAGE 122 FOR STEP-BY-STEP INSTRUCTIONS ON INSTALLING A HOT WATER CYLINDER**

▶ **SEE PAGE 124 FOR STEP-BY-STEP INSTRUCTIONS ON INSTALLING AN IMMERSION HEATER**

Instantaneous water heaters

Most modern hot water systems rely on a boiler to supply both hot water and central heating, but there are still many properties where hot water is supplied instantaneously through a multipoint gas or electric heater, or a single-point unit such as the familiar Ascot.

In fact, the modern combination boiler is essentially a multipoint unit with the addition of a central heating function. Hot water is supplied on demand, often temporarily cutting off the heat to the central heating in the process. However, there are many instances where the use of a water heating unit, separate from a central heating system, will provide an economical and practical solution to a hot water need. This is particularly the case where the 'point-of-use' is remote from the rest of the hot water system. The most common point-of-use electrical unit is, in fact, the instantaneous electric shower (see page 108), and exactly the same installation criteria apply to

the over- or under-sink water heater as to the electric shower. The only difference with the under-sink unit is the need for special taps and valves to deal with the expansion of water. In the over-sink water heater, expansion takes place through the spout, which must always remain open, the water flow being controlled on the inlet side. In the case of under-sink heaters, control is provided by the tap on the outlet, which prevents expansion in that direction.

There are gas instantaneous water heaters available, but since any work on gas appliances may only be carried out by a competent CORGI-registered installer, they are outside the scope of this book.

Sink-based. point-of-use electric water heaters are designed for hand washing and similar activities, and units range in power from about 3kW to over 7kW, the latter being a typical power rating for an electric shower. The electrical installation also follows the rules that apply to electric showers.

Typical of point-of-use water heaters is this Handy 3 unit, from Heatrae Sadia, with 3.1kW power rating.

Installing a hot water cylinder

When replacing an old hot water cylinder, it should be possible to obtain a good match of cylinder connection positions so that pipework modifications are minimal, but in some cases it will be worth labelling the pipes so that you know how to reconnect them. Take care when changing the cylinder to ensure that the walls of the new unit are not damaged when attaching the pipes – they are very thin and are easily damaged.

When removing the old cylinder, turn off the electricity supply before disconnecting the immersion heater (if fitted). Then turn off the water supply and drain the cylinder, using the drain valve at its base, not forgetting the heating circuit from the boiler with an indirect system. The latter will have a drain valve near the boiler. If the cylinder has no drain valve, the only solution is to siphon out the water, using a length of hose inserted through the boss in the top. Once the cylinder is empty, the pipes can be disconnected and it can be removed.

If the cylinder is fitted with an immersion heater, remove this and transfer it to the new cylinder (see page 124). Being made of copper, the old cylinder will have some scrap value, so it will pay you to look for a scrap dealer who will take it off your hands.

TOOLS AND MATERIALS

- ☐ Length of hose
- ☐ Adjustable spanner
- ☐ Screwdriver
- ☐ Immersion heater spanner
- ☐ PTFE tape
- ☐ Pipe connectors
- ☐ Copper pipe (possibly)
- ☐ Hot water cylinder

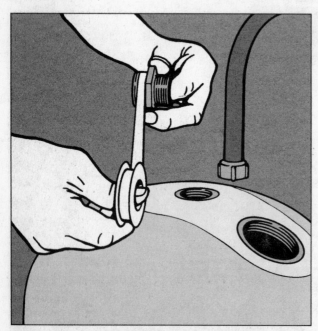

1 A cylinder full of water will weigh a considerable amount, so it must be supported by a firm base. If you are installing a cylinder in a completely new location, stout battens spanning the joist run will help spread the load and also allow air to circulate around the bottom of the cylinder. If you are replacing an existing cylinder, make sure that its support is strong enough to take the weight of the new cylinder.

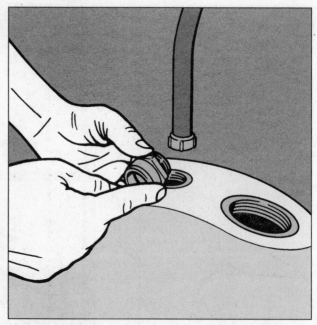

2 Fit a compression connector to the top of the cylinder for the feed and expansion pipe, wrapping its threads with two or three layers of PTFE tape to ensure a watertight seal. Tighten the connector in its boss with an adjustable spanner. It may be necessary to turn the cylinder to align the connector and pipe, but this may make other connections difficult, so be prepared to make changes to pipe runs.

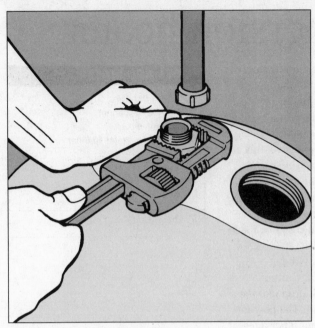

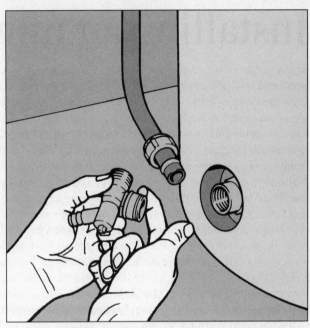

3 With the position of the feed and expansion pipe adjusted as necessary, connect the pipe to the connector in the top of the cylinder. Slip the capnut and olive of the connector onto the end of the pipe and tighten the capnut onto the fitting with an adjustable spanner. Don't over-tighten the nut, as this may cause a leak to develop. Take care not to dislodge the cylinder, either, as this may strain the connection.

4 The cold water supply enters the hot water cylinder at the bottom. Identify the boss in the side of the cylinder, then wrap the thread of the connector for the supply pipe with PTFE tape. Again, two or three layers should suffice. Screw the connector into the boss by hand. Then, finally tighten it with an adjustable spanner. If necessary, extend the supply pipe to the boss position.

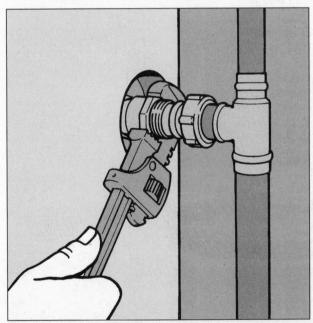

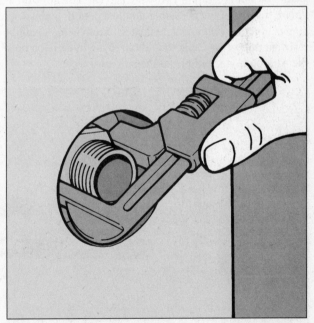

5 Rather than attaching the supply pipe directly to the cold feed connector, fit a drain valve to it, aligning the spout so that you can easily push a hose onto its end. This will allow you to drain the cylinder if the need should arise some time in the future. Then connect the supply pipe, making sure the compression connector is tight. Also ensure that there is a servicing valve on the supply pipe so that the system can be isolated easily.

6 With an indirect system, check the connectors for the boiler flow and return pipes, making sure that they are tight in their bosses. Then run in the pipes. If the cylinder has a boss for an immersion heater, fit the heater, adjust the thermostat, and reconnect the wiring. When all the connections have been made, refill the system by restoring the water supply and inspect the connections for signs of leakage.

Installing an immersion heater

Replacing an immersion heater is a relatively simple job. After shutting off the water and electricity to the cylinder, drain it to below the level of the lowest immersion heater boss (for a top-mounted heater, this will be just below the top of the cylinder; but for a bottom-mounted heater, almost the entire cylinder must be drained). The wiring should be disconnected, and the heater unscrewed, using an immersion heater spanner. Although inexpensive, this can be hired. The immersion heater is simply withdrawn from the cylinder and replaced by a new unit. A new thermostat should be fitted at the same time, but it may not be sold packaged with the heater unit (check when purchasing).

If your cylinder has no immersion heater, a new one may be installed, provided an existing boss is available. If not, a new connection could be made by using an Essex flange installed in the cylinder wall. However, an immersion heater should not be fitted to a direct self-priming cylinder.

After draining down, use a hole saw to drill the cylinder wall. Cutting through the thin metal of a cylinder is not easy, and debris will drop into the cylinder and may cause corrosion if not completely washed out. The position of the hole is also critical, as the immersion heater must not foul other internal parts of the cylinder. The job may be easier if the cylinder is removed.

The system will be out of action for some time while this work is carried out, and in these circumstances, it may be better simply to replace the cylinder altogether, particularly if it is quite old. It may be corroded and, almost certainly, will not have factory-fitted insulation.

The electrical circuit to the immersion heater must be independent and should be run in 2.5mm^2 twin-core and earth cable, with a 20 amp fuse or circuit breaker at the consumer unit to a double-pole switch or fused connection unit (with neon indicator). From here, a length of 15 amp heat-resistant three-core cable should run to the immersion heater. If the switch is in the bathroom, it should be of the pull-cord type.

TOOLS AND MATERIALS

- ☐ Length of hose
- ☐ Adjustable spanner
- ☐ Screwdriver
- ☐ Immersion heater spanner
- ☐ Electric drill
- ☐ Hole saw
- ☐ Essex flange
- ☐ PTFE tape
- ☐ Immersion heater
- ☐ Thermostat

Over a period of time, an immersion heater will suffer from corrosion, as shown here. Eventually, it will stop working altogether and will need replacing. This particular example has short heating elements and is designed for fitting horizontally into the cylinder. Sometimes, two such elements are fitted – one near the top, and one near the bottom – allowing part or all of the cylinder to be heated depending on hot water needs.

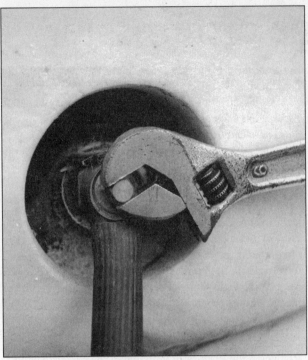

1 After turning off the water to the hot system, drain down the cylinder to below the bottom of the immersion heater boss. Fix a hose to the drain valve and run it outside to a convenient gully. Then open the valve. Don't forget to close it again.

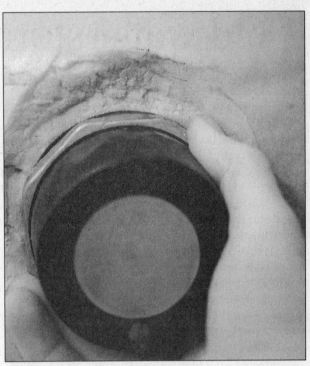

2 After turning off the electricity supply to the cylinder and disconnecting the wiring, loosen the old immersion heater with an immersion heater spanner. Then remove the heater, unscrewing it by hand.

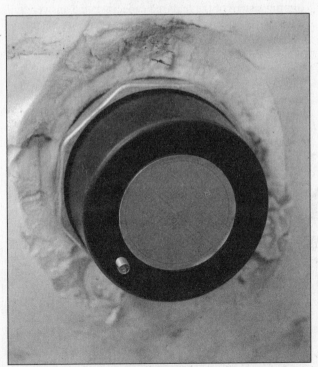

3 Wrap the thread of the new immersion heater with PTFE tape. Make sure the sealing washer is correctly seated on the heater body, then screw the replacement heater into place, tightening it with the spanner.

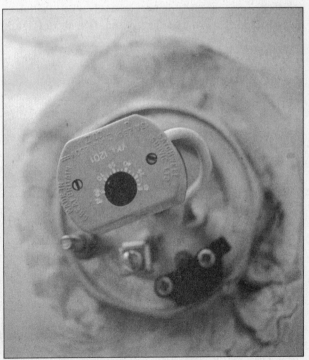

4 Check that the thermostat is in place and set it to 60°C, using a screwdriver blade inserted in the slot in the top of the unit. Then reconnect the wiring. Refill the cylinder and switch the electricity back on.

Cold water storage cisterns

Galvanised cisterns are susceptible to corrosion after a number of years in use. They should be inspected periodically, particularly if they have been in use for 15 years or more, and replaced as soon as a significant amount of rust is evident, indicating the breakdown of the protective coating.

Although new galvanised cisterns are available, modern practice is to replace them with plastic units. These do not corrode, they are cheaper and lighter in weight, and most important, they come with accessories to meet the requirements of the Water Byelaws. The regulations specify that the cistern must be covered to exclude light, insects, etc, yet still be open to the atmosphere.

If a cistern has to be changed, it offers the ideal opportunity to consider installing an alternative type of system – mains pressure, unvented, etc – that will not only dispense with the cistern in the loft and associated risks of freezing, but could also provide much higher performance from showers, etc. However, such a change may not be suitable if the local water pressure is low, or if the shower is already served from the cistern by a pump.

Support

Galvanised cisterns are often supported on substantial bearers laid across the loft joists. The strength and rigidity of the material is sufficient to support the weight of water contained in the cistern.

A plastic cistern must be supported across the whole of its base, on a board that is not likely to be affected by dampness caused by condensation. The board may be conveniently supported by the bearers for the old cistern.

Pipe sizes

When inspecting the existing system, measure the pipe sizes to check whether they are of metric (15, 22 or 28mm) or the old imperial dimensions. If the pipe sizes are imperial, any ¾ or 1in pipe will need an adaptor (¾in to 22mm; 1in to 28mm) so that it can be connected to the metric pipe that will be necessary for connection to the metric fittings purchased with the new cistern.

Cistern size

Replacing the old cistern with one of the same size will minimise modifications to the pipework. However, the old cistern may have been installed before the loft hatch was built, and it may not be possible to pass a standard cistern of the correct size through the hatch. A long, narrow cistern of the required capacity is the answer, and these are readily available from plumbers' merchants.

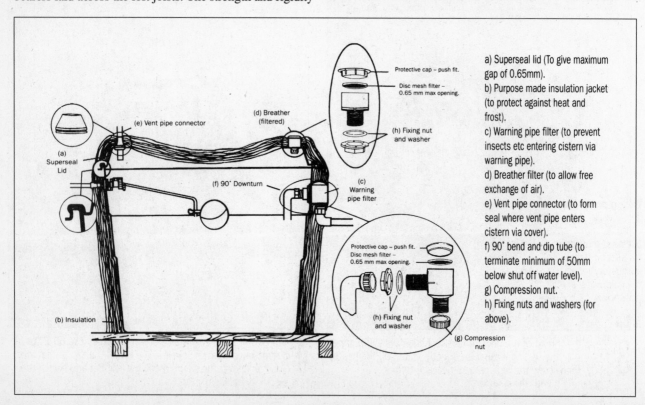

a) Superseal lid (To give maximum gap of 0.65mm).
b) Purpose made insulation jacket (to protect against heat and frost).
c) Warning pipe filter (to prevent insects etc entering cistern via warning pipe).
d) Breather filter (to allow free exchange of air).
e) Vent pipe connector (to form seal where vent pipe enters cistern via cover).
f) 90° bend and dip tube (to terminate minimum of 50mm below shut off water level).
g) Compression nut.
h) Fixing nuts and washers (for above).

Removing the old cistern

To replace the cistern, the water must be turned off at the main stopvalve, unless the pipe to the cistern has been fitted with a servicing valve. If so, turn it off to leave the supply to the kitchen in use.

The cistern must be drained by opening the cold tap on the bath (if the cold supply system is indirect), or the hot tap (if direct). Once drained, the cistern will still contain an amount of water in the bottom, which may spill out when the pipes are removed. You may be able to bale most of the water from the cistern with a cup or similar.

Next remove the pipes from the cistern. This may prove difficult, since they will have been in place for many years. If the pipes are to imperial sizes, simply cut them at a convenient place, and fit the imperial/metric adaptors (except to ½in pipes, which do not need them). Otherwise, undo the fittings ready for fitting to the new tank, or cut the pipes as appropriate.

Carefully move the old cistern out of the way. The cistern may have to remain in the loft if the hatch size is too small; unless you are very short of space, there is little point in trying to saw it up to allow removal.

▶ **SEE PAGE 128 FOR STEP-BY-STEP INSTRUCTIONS ON INSTALLING A COLD WATER CISTERN**

Above *A modern loft hatch may not be large enough to permit the passage of a cistern of conventional shape. For such situations, longer versions of small cross-section are available. (All illustrations courtesy T & D Trident)*

Facing page *Components of a cold water cistern that complies with the Water Byelaws, showing the installation details. The mandatory servicing valve on the cold water supply pipe is not shown.*

Right *Cutaway of a typical cold water cistern, showing the filtered breather inlet on top, the overflow warning pipe filter on the side, and the insulating jacket.*

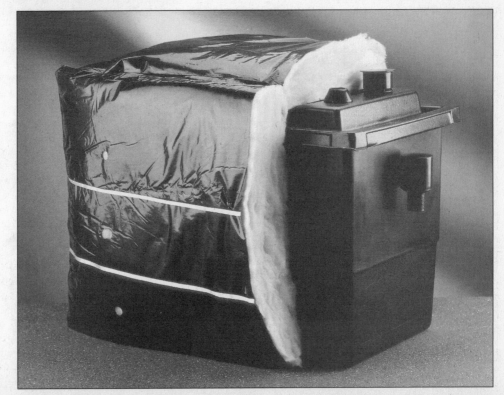

Installing a cold water cistern

Before installing a new cistern, lay its base board across the bearers of the old cistern, or the loft joists. Tongued-and-grooved floorboarding is ideal for the support, but any similar stout timber will do; don't use man-made boards that may suffer from condensation. Then place the cistern in position.

Mark the centres of the holes for the pipe connectors for the water supply, overflow warning pipe, and exit pipes. Cut these holes with a hole saw or wood bit of the correct size. A block of timber held behind the cistern wall while it is being drilled will prevent the wall from flexing, and help to produce a clean edge to each hole. Make sure that all the debris is removed from the cistern before it is filled.

At this point, consider whether other exit pipes may be needed in the near future, perhaps for a shower or bidet. If so, drill the appropriate holes, and fit each with a connector, a short length of pipe and a gate or ball valve. Use a stop end to seal off the pipe until it is needed.

Connect the remaining pipes to the cistern, ensuring that a servicing valve is fitted to the incoming cold water supply to the float valve. This is a requirement of the Water Byelaws. Exit pipes must also be fitted with gate or ball valves, allowing any particular section of pipework to be isolated in the event of a problem.

Check that all connections have been made and are secure. Then turn on the water supply. As the cistern fills, check for any leaks, tightening connections as necessary. Make sure that the float valve shuts off the water when the level is about 25mm (1in) below the level of the overflow warning pipe. Adjust the float arm or valve if required.

Make sure that the lid, insect screens, etc, are all in place. Then fit the insulation to both cistern and pipes.

TOOLS AND MATERIALS

- ☐ Tape measure and pencil
- ☐ Bradawl
- ☐ Electric drill
- ☐ Hole saw
- ☐ Half-round and rat-tail files
- ☐ Wire wool
- ☐ Pipe cutter
- ☐ Adjustable spanners
- ☐ PTFE tape
- ☐ Cistern with lid and fittings
- ☐ Float valve
- ☐ Tank connectors
- ☐ Copper pipe and connectors
- ☐ Gate or stop valves
- ☐ Insulating jacket

1 With the cistern in place, check the positions of the existing pipes. They may need cutting to length or repositioning slightly.

2 Having marked the centres of the various outlet holes, cut them to the correct size with a hole saw and electric drill.

3 Clean up the edges of each hole with a half-round file. Check the fit of the connector, opening up the hole slightly if necessary.

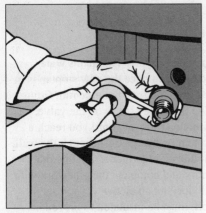

4 With the sealing washer in place on the connector, wind some PTFE tape around the thread to ensure a watertight seal.

5 Insert the connector through the hole from inside the cistern, fit the second sealing washer and add the nut, tightening it fully.

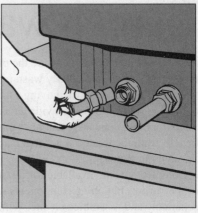

6 Cut a short length of pipe for each outlet connector. After deburring the pipe, fit an olive and attach the pipe to the connector with its capnut.

7 Fit a gate or stop valve to each outlet pipe, holding the body of the valve with one spanner while you tighten the nut with another.

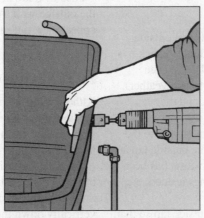

8 Cut holes near the top of the cistern for the float valve and overflow pipe. To prevent the walls from flexing, support them with a block of wood.

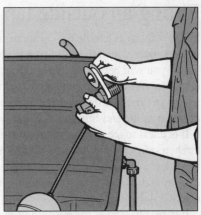

9 Fit the sealing washer to the shank of the float valve. Then wind PTFE tape around the thread. Insert the shank through the hole in the cistern wall.

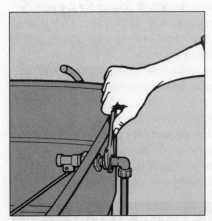

10 Secure the float valve to the cistern. Then run in the supply pipe and connect it to the valve. The pipe must be fitted with a servicing valve.

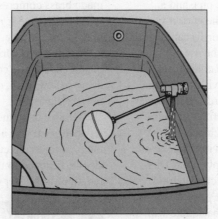

11 Check all connections, then turn on the water and allow the cistern to fill. Make sure the outlet valves are turned off.

12 Assemble the overflow pipe filter and dip tube. Then fit the lid, connect the vent pipe and lag the cistern with its jacket.

Garden water supplies

A supply of mains water outside the property will make many jobs easier, particularly washing the car and watering the garden. Also, having some means of collecting rainwater will provide a ready supply for watering more delicate greenhouse plants, which may not benefit from the treated water that reaches out homes through the mains.

Complete kits are available for installing an outside tap, or the various plumbing components may be bought separately and assembled on site. Whichever method is chosen, the pipework must include a double check valve to prevent back-siphonage, which is a requirement of the Water Byelaws. In most kits, this is incorporated in the valve that provides the connection with the mains supply.

Fitting an outside tap

If you want to assemble the components for an outside water supply yourself, in addition to the double check valve, you will need a bib tap and back plate, a drain elbow (to allow the pipe to be drained in frosty weather), a stoptap (to allow the run to be isolated), and the necessary pipe and fittings.

It is usual to tee a branch from the mains supply to the kitchen (after the kitchen tap), and to fit the outside tap at the nearest convenient point. Once this position has been determined, the necessary pipe runs, fittings needed, etc, can be established.

It is best to start at the position of the outside tap so that the last job is the connection to the water supply. First, decide where to fit the back plate to the wall, then drill a hole some inches above the plate for the supply pipe to pass through the wall. A hole of about 25mm (1in) in diameter will be needed to take both the pipe and a protective sleeve of plastic or copper. The easiest way of achieving this is with a core drill. Such drills can be hired. Alternatively, a large masonry drill can be used to make a pilot hole, which can be enlarged with a cold chisel and club hammer. Using this latter method will require the wall to be filled and made good afterwards, both inside and out, using sand and cement mortar, filler or foam sealer. The core drill will produce a much neater job.

Once the hole has been made, line it with a sleeve of copper or plastic pipe to protect the supply pipe. Then drill and plug the wall, and screw the back plate into position, using brass screws. Cut a piece of pipe to pass through the sleeve, connecting it to the backplate with a 90 degree elbow and a short vertical pipe.

Inside, isolate the water supply, tee off a horizontal branch from the rising main, and fit the stopvalve as close

as is convenient to the main supply. The mains water supply may be turned on again once the new stoptap is in place and itself turned off. Continue the pipe run, fitting the double check valve (note the arrows on the valve, which indicate the direction of flow), until you reach a point directly below the pipe that passes through the wall. Fit the drain elbow at this point (which should be the lowest point on the run), and complete the pipework with another short vertical pipe and an elbow.

All outside pipework must be insulated to prevent it from freezing (minimum wall thickness 25mm/1in), using closed-cell pipe insulation, which does not absorb moisture. For a neater job, box-in this pipework with wood and paint it to match the house decoration.

Also insulate the inside pipework where it runs close to the outside wall. Again, box-in the pipework for a neater appearance, but make sure that the drain valve and stopvalve are readily accessible.

A remote outside tap

Although the simplest installation is to mount the tap on the house wall, it may be more convenient to site the tap some distance from the house. In this case, the pipework must be run underground to protect it from frost damage.

Tee into the mains supply, as for a wall-mounted tap, but drop the pipe to floor level before passing it through the wall. Fit a 90 degree elbow, then run the pipe vertically down the outside wall and into the ground. Take the pipe to a minimum depth of 450mm (18in) to protect it from frost and accidental damage from by digging. Run the pipe in a trench of that depth to the desired location.

Use plastic pipe (MDPE or polybutylene) with purpose-made brass compression or plastic fittings for the outside run. Plastic pipe is more resistant to bursting when frozen than is copper pipe, and it is also more resistant to corrosion when buried in the ground. Begin the run of plastic pipe at the connector just inside the house wall, if using MDPE pipe, or at the mains tee when installing polybutylene pipe.

The tap can be mounted on a convenient wall or wooden post. Use a bib tap and back plate as before. Run the pipe up to the tap inside an insulated, protective sleeve, fastened to the wall or post with suitable clips. A length of rainwater downpipe is ideal for the sleeve.

▶ **SEE PAGE 132 FOR STEP-BY-STEP INSTRUCTIONS ON INSTALLING AN OUTSIDE TAP KIT**

Various purpose-designed diverters are available for connecting a downpipe to a water butt. Most are designed to redirect the flow into the downpipe when the butt is full. This is usually achieved by incorporating some form of weir into the body of the unit.

Collecting rainwater for the greenhouse and garden

Although water from the mains supply can be used for watering the garden, rainwater is much better for the plants, and also for topping-up garden ponds during dry weather. The chemicals used to treat water to make it suitable for human consumption can actually have a detrimental effect on plants and pond life.

Fortunately, a supply of rainwater for use in dry spells is easily created, using water butts and/or storage tanks connected to the rainwater system of the house or an outbuilding. If a butt is actually placed inside a greenhouse, it will contain water at the same temperature. This will ensure the minimum of shock to plants when they are being watered.

All that needs to be done is to divert the rainwater from a downpipe, using a purpose-designed diverter or offset bends, into the butt or tank. During prolonged periods of rain, the butt will soon fill, so provision must be made to prevent the water from overflowing. Some ready-made diverters are designed to direct water back into the downpipe automatically when the butt is full; others can be opened manually to direct water to the butt, and then closed when it is full. If the downpipe discharges directly into the butt, a simple overflow pipe can be installed and run to a nearby drain or soakaway.

The butt itself should be stood on blocks to allow sufficient room for a watering can to be placed under the tap. In the greenhouse, the tank could be sunk into the ground to allow easier access for a watering can beneath the staging.

Regardless of position, all butts and tanks should be securely covered to prevent accidents. A tight-fitting cover will also exclude light, preventing the growth of green algae, and stop insects from breeding in the water.

Fitting an outside tap kit

A modern outside tap kit will make the installation of a garden water supply a simple job that can be tackled by anyone. The kit will include all of the items necessary to make the installation.

Essentially, the kit comprises a self-cutting valve to make the connection to the rising main, a length of flexible high-pressure hose to take the supply to a rigid plastic pipe that passes through the wall, and a bib tap and back plate for fitting to the wall. A double check valve is incorporated in the self-cutting valve to prevent back-siphonage.

The only restriction in using a kit is the length of the flexible hose, making it necessary to install the tap within a relatively short distance of the rising main (usually no more than 1.2m/4ft). However, the hose also makes it easy to drain the pipework for the winter, since its connectors need only be tightened onto their couplings by hand. Having turned off the water supply at the valve, all you need do is release one end of the hose and allow the water to drain from it.

The self-cutting valve is designed to allow you to connect it to the rising main without having to turn off the water supply and without any risk of leaks. Thus the installation can be made very quickly, with the minimum of disruption to the household. Moreover, if you use a core drill to bore through the wall for the rigid pipe, very little making good (if any) will be required.

Once all the connections have been made, the outside tap should be opened and the water slowly turned on at the self-cutting valve. If there are no leaks, the tap can be turned off and the system brought into use.

TOOLS AND MATERIALS

☐ Tape measure
☐ Pencil
☐ Electric drill
☐ Core drill
☐ Masonry bit
☐ Screwdriver
☐ Hacksaw
☐ Half-round and rat-tail files
☐ Wire wool
☐ Screws
☐ Wall plugs
☐ PTFE tape
☐ Outside tap kit

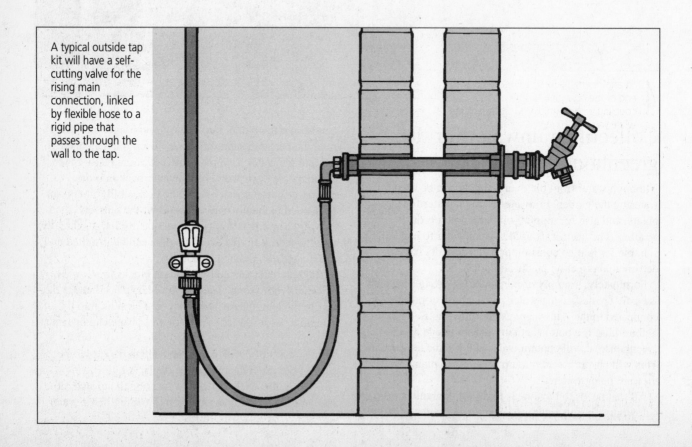

A typical outside tap kit will have a self-cutting valve for the rising main connection, linked by flexible hose to a rigid pipe that passes through the wall to the tap.

1 Drill the hole for the rigid supply pipe (from the inside), cut the pipe to length and push it through the hole. Fit the metal support insert to its end.

2 Fit the wall plate to the end of the pipe, and mark its fixing holes on the wall. Drill and plug the holes, then screw the plate to the wall.

3 Screw the tap shank into the wall plate socket, having first wrapped PTFE tape around its thread to prevent any leaks. Set the tap upright.

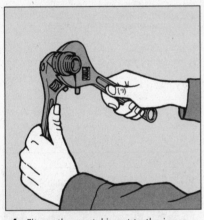

4 Fit another metal insert to the inner end of the rigid pipe. Then hold the coupling with an adjustable spanner while you tighten its nut with another.

5 Check that the sealing washer is seated correctly in the connector, and screw the flexible high-pressure hose to the coupling.

6 Decide where you will break into the rising main. Then fit the clamp of the self-cutting valve around the pipe, making sure that it is tight.

7 Check that the valve is turned off, and screw it into its socket. As you do so, it will cut into the pipe; there is no need to turn off the water supply.

8 Adjust the angle of the valve to suit the incoming flexible hose. Then tighten its locknut with a spanner to prevent it from moving.

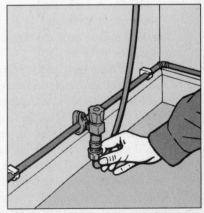

9 Screw the high-pressure hose onto the valve outlet, making sure the sealing washer is in place. Then turn on the valve and check for leaks.

Removing a rainwater system

Set high on the building and exposed to all weathers, the rainwater system of your home leads a hard life and, if not maintained to a high standard, it will eventually deteriorate and cease to function as it should. Unfortunately, because it is relatively inaccessible, the system often does not receive the attention it deserves. As a result, leaks may develop from the joints between lengths of guttering, sections may break away following impact from ladders or as a result of severe rusting, and downpipes may come adrift from the gutter outlet and the wall.

Although repairs can often be made by applying mastic to leaking joints, remaking connections with downpipes, and patching broken sections with glassfibre repair kits, these can only be considered a short-term solution. Eventually, the problems will return, and may be even worse. The real answer is to replace the old system with a new plastic one.

First, however, the old system must be removed, and if it is of cast iron (as in this step-by-step sequence), you must take particular care because of the heavy weight of the individual components. Likewise, an asbestos cement system will need special precautions.

Once the old system has been removed, the fascia boards can be inspected for their condition; some may show signs of rot or damage, in which case, they must be replaced with new boards. Take the opportunity, too, to fill any holes and paint the boards before installing the new guttering. Also make good any damage to the wall following removal of the downpipe.

TOOLS AND MATERIALS
☐ Hammer
☐ Screwdriver
☐ Adjustable spanner
☐ Junior hacksaw
☐ Electric drill and HSS bits (possibly)
☐ Wrecking bar
☐ Ladder or access tower

SAFETY FIRST

Working on a rainwater system can be a risky business because of its height from the ground. You must arrange a suitable form of safe access, and follow these guidelines:

● All work on rainwater systems involves the use of a ladder or, far better, an access tower. If you have no head for heights, or are worried about working at the top of a ladder, call in a contractor to do the job.

● When working on a ladder, you must make sure that the feet are resting on firm ground, and someone should stand at the foot to steady the ladder. Never rest the ladder on the guttering – even if made of cast iron – but use a stand-off and, if possible, fasten the ladder to the wall.

● If working on a cast iron system, remember that the individual components will be very heavy. They will require some strength to remove or replace, even when using extra nails as supports on the fascia. If dropped, they can cause quite serious damage and injury.

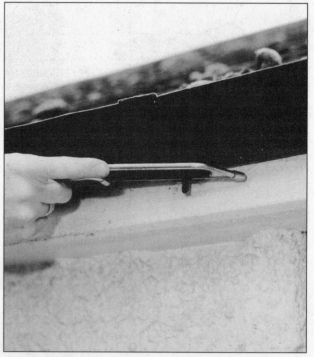

3 Remove the bolts securing the lengths of cast iron guttering. It is highly likely that they will be rusted solid, so the only solution is to saw off the bolt ends with a hacksaw. Then tap out the remainder of the bolt.

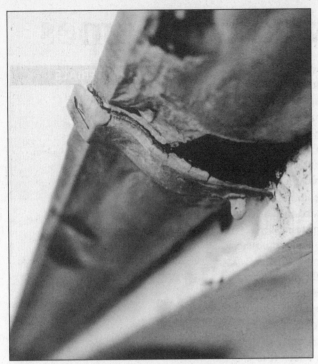

1 Any parts of an existing rainwater system that are damaged, or are leaking, should be replaced as soon as possible to prevent damage to the building. (All photographs courtesy Marley Extrusions)

2 Unless a joint is being made to a socket, cast iron guttering normally has to be cut with a hacksaw. For safety, the section being cut should be supported; a large nail temporarily driven into the fascia should do, provided the fascia itself is sound.

4 Lengths of cast iron guttering will be very heavy, so take down only one section at a time. Remove the screws holding the guttering to the fascia, and pass the section down to a helper below. If the screws are rusted, you will have to drill them out.

5 Once all the guttering has been removed, the downpipe may be prised from the wall, using a wrecking bar. Apply the minimum of force necessary to reduce damage, which will have to be made good later.

Fitting guttering and downpipes

Although plastic rainwater systems will eventually become brittle with age and exposure to the elements, in the main they require much less attention than other materials, which makes them a prime choice when replacing an old system. They come in a range of basic colours, but can also be painted to match the decor of your house if required. Being light in weight they are also easy to install

Several manufacturers produce plastic rainwater systems, and while they are made to standard nominal sizes, components from different manufacturers may not always be compatible with each other, so stick to one make. However, most ranges include adaptors that allow connection to standard cast iron systems. Thus, if you live in a semi-detached or terraced property, you will be able to connect your system to your neighbour's without any problems.

Before removing the old system, it is worth obtaining a manufacturer's catalogue from a local builders' merchant, as this will list all the components of the system, giving their sizes and uses. Having measured the run of guttering required, and the height of the downpipe, you will be able to use the catalogue to plan your new system and then list all the parts you need.

Plastic rainwater systems are simply clipped and pushed together, rubber seals being fitted to the gutter connectors to ensure leak-proof joints. If any guttering or a downpipe needs cutting to length, this is simply done with a fine-toothed saw. Once any burrs have been removed from the cut end, the section will be ready for use.

TOOLS AND MATERIALS

- ☐ Tape measure
- ☐ Pencil
- ☐ Spirit level
- ☐ Bradawl
- ☐ Screwdriver
- ☐ String line
- ☐ Fine-toothed saw
- ☐ Half-round file
- ☐ Electric drill
- ☐ Masonry bit
- ☐ Rustproof screws
- ☐ Wall plugs
- ☐ Guttering, downpipes and accessories

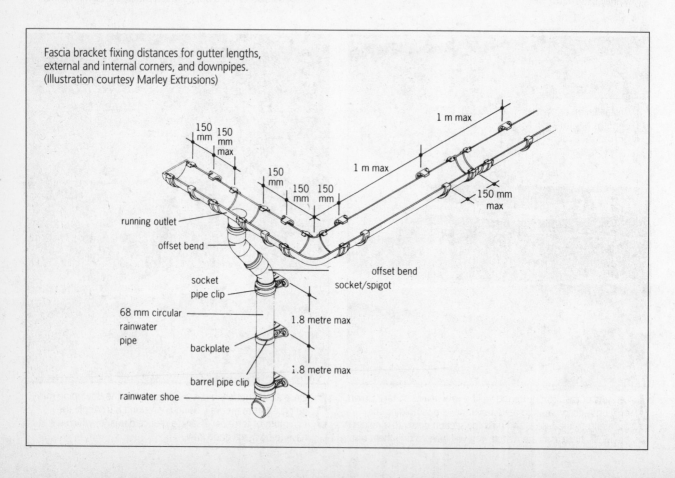

Fascia bracket fixing distances for gutter lengths, external and internal corners, and downpipes.
(Illustration courtesy Marley Extrusions)

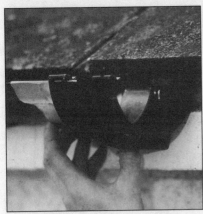

1 A specially-designed gutter adaptor is needed when joining new guttering to existing guttering. (All photographs courtesy Marley Extrusions)

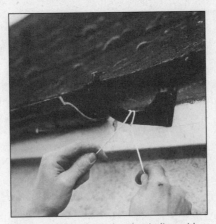

2 Fix the first fascia bracket in line with the old guttering, and stretch a string line between this bracket and another at the end of the run.

3 Position Intermediate brackets at no more than 1m (3ft) centres, and set them so that the guttering slopes at about 1:600 towards the outlet.

4 Install union brackets where two lengths of guttering will meet. These incorporate rubber seals to prevent any leakage from the joint.

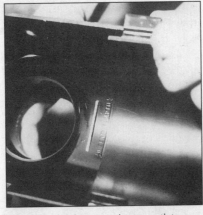

5 When joining guttering to outlets or unions, make sure that the end of the gutter aligns with the insertion depth mark on the fitting.

6 Fit the guttering into the brackets, hooking the back edge under the bracket lip and snapping the clip over the front. Add stop ends as necessary.

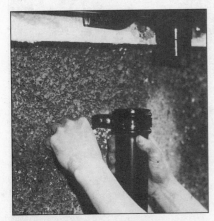

7 Fix the top section of the downpipe below the gutter outlet, using a socket pipe clip. Attach this to the wall with rustproof screws.

8 Fix the remainder of the downpipe to the wall with barrel pipe clips. Add a shoe to the bottom if the pipe discharges into a gully.

9 When connecting the gutter outlet to the offset bend at the top of the downpipe, you may find it easier if you unclip the outlet from its brackets.

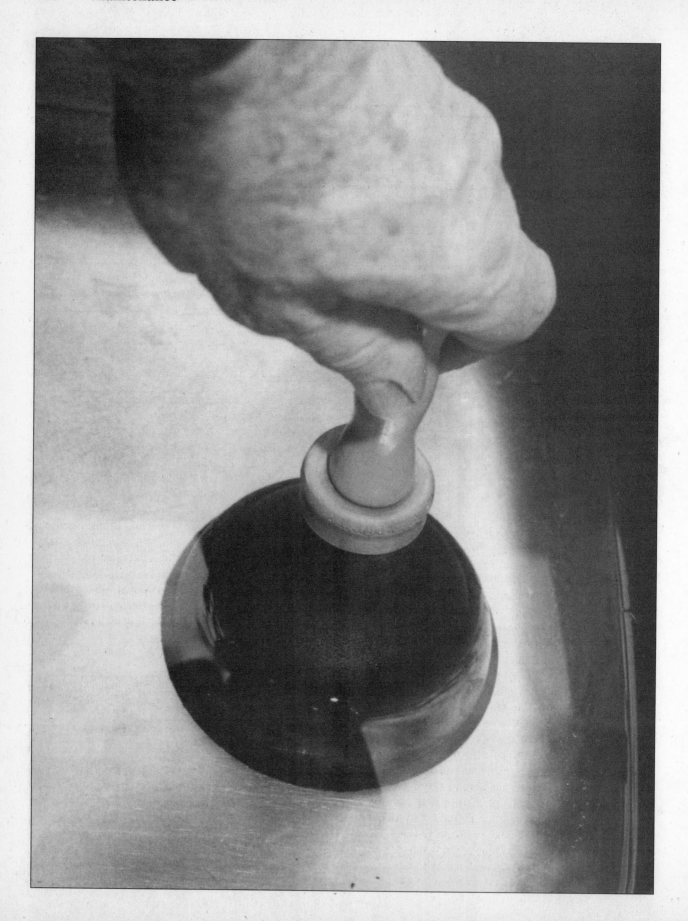

Chapter 6

Maintenance
Leaks and blockages

Good planning and preparation are the keys to dealing with a plumbing emergency. Fast, effective action as soon as the emergency occurs can save considerable distress and expense.

Most problems with the water supply or waste system in a property begin as minor inconveniences – the dripping tap or leaking joint – and may, in fact, never become catastrophic. Even a blocked drain will normally give some sign that a problem is developing. A bad odour, or waste not flowing away as quickly as it normally does, should alert the householder that something is wrong, and that investigation is needed. However, when a major failure does occur, it is essential that the correct action is taken quickly to minimise damage, not just to decorations and furniture, but also to the fabric of the building.

Serious damage

Burst pipes are the greatest potential source of serious damage from the plumbing system in the home. For example, if the mains supply to the water storage cistern should burst in the loft, and it was left unchecked for 24 hours, between 68,000 and 136,000 litres (15,000 and 30,000 gallons) of water could be flooded onto the ceiling. In such circumstances, it is not surprising for ceilings to collapse, and the contents of the property to be ruined in a very short time. Even with the leak beyond the cistern of an indirect system, water will continue to be fed by the mains supply through the cistern, although not at mains pressure. Flow through the leak will depend on the head of water between the leak and the cistern. Although the rate of flow will be much lower, unfortunately the potential for damage may not be reduced accordingly.

Fortunately, such catastrophes are becoming less frequent because of better insulation and heating in our homes. Even so, it is important to remember that, at temperatures below freezing point, insulation can only *delay* the onset of freezing in the absence of an adequate supply of heat. If a pipe containing standing water is kept below freezing point for long enough, it will freeze no matter how thick is the insulation around the pipe.

However, bursts and leaks do not always occur in winter, nor is their presence always immediately obvious at the time the damage is done. For example, it is quite possible for a pipe, under floorboards or in a wall, to be pierced accidentally by a nail. Yet the pipe may not show signs of a leak for a considerable time, possibly even years, until the nail has corroded away or has been moved, perhaps by someone knocking nail heads flush to the floorboards on renovation or laying carpet.

Effective action

When faced with a leak of any kind, follow these steps to deal with the problem effectively:

● Turn off the water supply at the stoptap. If the leak is on the mains supply, this should immediately stop water flowing from the leak. If it is on an indirect system, fed by a cistern in the loft or similar, closing the stoptap prevents water from replenishing the cistern and feeding the leaking pipe.
● Find a torch and/or candles, and turn off the electricity supply. Water can easily find its way to the electrical system, creating a potentially lethal hazard.
● Find the source of the leak, assuming it is not already obvious. If it is on the indirect system, either isolate the section at the appropriate valve, or drain down the system to below the level of the leak by turning on the bath and other taps.
● Fix the leak and refill the system.

Emergency toolkit

☐ Torch
☐ Pliers (to twist wire)
☐ Saw or pipe cutter (compact type for working in close quarters)
☐ Endstops
☐ Hose
☐ Jubilee clips (appropriate sizes)
☐ Screwdriver

Permanent repairs

The best way to effect a permanent repair is to cut out the damaged section of pipe, and replace it with a new piece. Joints may be made by soldering (using end-feed or solder-ring fittings), or by using compression fittings or push-fit fittings. In all cases, the pipe will have to be sprung into the fittings.

Alternatively, proprietary pipe repair kits or fittings may be used. The latter are designed so that they can be compressed to be fitted to one piece of pipe, then extended to join the other pipe, thus avoiding the difficulties of springing a length of relatively rigid pipe into a pair of fittings.

Temporary repairs

All too often, leaks occur at the most inconvenient times, usually after the local hardware store has closed. However, there are several methods of making temporary repairs to a leaking pipe until such time as a permanent repair can be effected. If the leak is a small one, you can deal with it effectively by following these steps:

● Slit a short length of plastic hosepipe, fit it over the pipe with the slit on the opposite side to the leak, and fasten it in place with Jubilee clips or twists of strong copper wire, fitted at several places along the pipe. (Earth wire from 240 volt cable may be suitable.)

● Special resin-based pipe repair materials, suitably reinforced and wrapped around the pipe, may provide a seal when set. (Copper wire wound around the repair may also help.)

● If that section of the system is not needed until a permanent repair can be made, and in the absence of a stopvalve, cut the pipe above and below the leak, and fit stop ends to both pieces of pipe. Speedfit endstop fittings are ideal for this purpose; compression versions are also suitable, but they will take a little longer to fit.

Leaking taps

Leaks from the system may not always occur because of damage to the pipework and fittings; the taps and valves may also cause problems through wear and tear, and old age. It is an offence under the Water Byelaws to allow a tap to continue to leak, because it is a waste of water. For those on metered water supplies, it is also expensive, since a steadily dripping tap loses a surprisingly large amount of water. If a dripping tap lost 4.5 litres (1 gallon) per hour, over the course of a year, 40,000 litres (8736 gallons) would be lost.

Also, in cold weather, the dripping water can freeze and block the waste pipe, which may result in an overflow when the tap unfreezes. The blocked pipe will take much longer to thaw out.

LEAKS
BE PREPARED

1 **Know where the stoptap is,** and how to turn it off.

2 **Make sure that the rest of the household knows where the stoptap is,** and how to turn it off.

3 Maintain the stoptap to ensure that it remains free to operate, by turning it one or two turns every three or four months. **Never leave it in its fully open position,** as it may seize more readily when fully open. Just a quarter turn off will prevent jamming, yet still provide virtually full flow.

4 **Know your system** and the positions of all the valves.

► SEE PAGE 144 FOR STEP-BY-STEP
INSTRUCTIONS ON
RE-WASHERING A TAP

Taps can leak from two points. A leak from the top when the tap is open means that the gland packing around the spindle needs replacing. However, a leak from the spout when the tap is closed means that the washer or the washer seat, or both, have worn. Kitchen sink mixer taps, which have a swivelling spout, may leak from the joint between the spout and the body, indicating a failed O-ring seal or washer.

To replace the gland packing or O-ring means removing the tap head and cover, or the spout in the case of the sink mixer. It is not normally necessary to turn the water off to replace the packing.

With the kitchen tap, the swivel spout either pulls out or unscrews to reveal the O-ring, or rings. These must be replaced with rings of the correct size, and lubricated with silicone grease. With some kitchen taps, circlip pliers may be necessary to gain access to the rings.

On modern non-rising spindle types, the packing usually takes the form of an O-ring, which is simple to replace after removing the head. On older types of tap, the packing may be a washer or hemp, or similar, and can be replaced with either greased hemp (if available) or well-greased wool.

Occasionally, tightening the gland nut on older taps will stop a leak; if not, the packing must be replaced. However, before replacing either packing or washer, the tap head must be removed. With a shrouded-head tap, this is normally a matter of either pulling the head off (from a splined shaft), or of lifting the coloured disc on the head and releasing a small screw.

Problems usually arise with older cross-head types. The cross-head is secured by a small grub screw, which may be difficult to unscrew. The head itself may also resist movement, even after a gentle tap with a hammer. If this happens, the cover over the tap body should be unscrewed after the tap has been opened fully, pieces of wood of appropriate thickness inserted between the tap cover and the tap body, and the tap turned off, which forces off the head. It may be possible to loosen the cover itself by hand, or you may need a wrench to shift it; if so, it must be protected against damage by wrapping it in a cloth or other soft material.

Make sure you know the location of your stoptap; turn the handle regularly to ensure free movement.

Water hammer

The rapid closing of a tap or valve, especially those valves controlling the filling of washing machines or dishwashers and quarter-turn ceramic disc taps, can set up a shock wave in the water of susceptible pipework. When this hits the end of the run, it produces considerable noise – water hammer. A similar situation with the float valve in a cistern can set up a self-perpetuating series of waves and rebounds, producing the familiar banging noise of water hammer.

In some circumstances, water hammer may be severe enough to damage fittings, particularly those on washing machine hoses. In this case, the fitting may even be pushed off the connection to the machine, causing considerable leakage.

Several solutions are available, depending on the cause:

● With hammer caused by the float valve of a cistern, fixing the pipe more firmly to the cistern may solve the problem.

● Another possibility is to change the direction of the pipework by introducing bends that appear to damp down the shock wave. On a washing machine, simply coiling the connecting pipes may cure the problem.

● If these options fail, fit a water hammer arrester as close as possible to the source of the hammer. This is a device that absorbs the shock wave – effectively by compressing air in a closed tube.

● Generally, water hammer can be minimised by keeping pipe runs short, and making sure that pipes are firmly supported.

► SEE PAGE 146 FOR STEP-BY-STEP
INSTRUCTIONS ON REPLACING A
CERAMIC DISC CARTRIDGE

► SEE PAGE 148 FOR STEP-BY-STEP
INSTRUCTIONS ON REPLACING
FLOAT VALVE WASHERS

Clearing blocked waste systems: Sinks and basins

A sink or basin will not normally become blocked without advance warning; the water not running away quite as fast as it used to do is a good indication that all is not well. If this is noticed, preventative action should be taken as soon as possible.

Filling the sink or basin with very hot water and detergent may be sufficient to clear the beginnings of a blockage before it becomes a serious problem. If not, the trap should be removed, checked and cleaned (with the sink empty, and a bowl or bucket under the trap to catch any water). A quick look down the waste pipe after disconnecting the trap (a small torch will probably be needed) will show if a build-up has occurred in the pipe close to the trap, and what further action is necessary.

Various chemical cleaners are available, but as most are caustic, they must be used with caution. Wear protective rubber gloves and goggles to protect your skin and eyes. They are not as effective as mechanical methods for clearing obstructions, but may be used on partially cleaned pipe to finish the cleaning process. These cleaners should not be used on systems where the waste is collected in a septic tank.

Bacteria-based treatments that digest grease are available and do not, apparently, hinder the action of a septic tank. However, their effectiveness and safety in the area of the domestic sink may be questionable.

Some people like to keep waste systems clear by applying washing soda every month or so. Again, this treatment is not suitable for use in a septic tank system.

If chemical methods fail, mechanical methods must be employed. The first tool to use is the simple plunger, which forces a quantity of water or air, trapped in the rubber bell, into the waste pipe, pressurising it for a second or two. With most blockages, this is sufficient to shift the obstruction and allow water to flow. When using a plunger, the overflow inlet must be covered firmly with a wet cloth to prevent the water from being squirted back into the sink. A plunger will need some water in the sink or basin to work effectively; a depth of about 50mm (2in) is usually enough.

Various hand pumps are also available for clearing blockages. These perform much the same action as the plunger, using the shock of released compressed air to dislodge the obstruction.

If repeated use of a plunger or pump does not work, the next step is to remove the trap or its cleaning eye, if fitted. It is fairly easy to dismantle modern plastic traps, since they can be unscrewed from the waste outlet and pipe. However, with old-fashioned metal traps, it can be almost impossible to gain access if the cleaning eye is corroded onto the trap. In this situation, the use of force must be

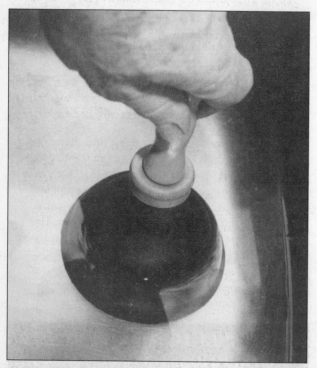

If a sink, basin, bath or shower waste becomes blocked, it can often be cleared with the aid of a plunger.

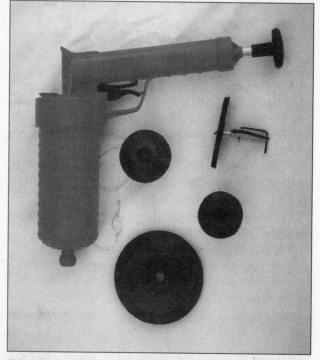

This tool 'shoots' a jet of air into a blocked pipe to break up and force away the blockage.

limited to avoid damaging the sink or the trap, particularly if the waste system is run in lead pipe.

If you cannot remove a cleaning eye, or if it is a bath or shower waste that is blocked and you cannot get a bucket under the trap, then recourse to a plumber's 'snake' will be necessary. This may be a coiled or flat length of flexible spring steel, one end of which is inserted into the waste pipe, and rotated by a handle at the other end. As it meets the obstruction, it will loosen the blockage and push it towards the drain until the pipe is cleared.

These tools are available for hire, but it may be useful to include a small one in your tool kit. In an emergency, a reasonable lightweight substitute can be made from curtain wire with a hook screwed into the end. A metal coathanger, suitably straightened, may also be useful for clearing blockages at the trap, but unlike the curtain wire and snake, it will not pass around the sharp bends found in the trap. When working on plastic pipes, a coathanger should be used with care to avoid damaging the pipe.

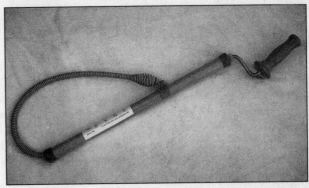

This hand-operated drain spring can be used for clearing small pipes.

WCs

A properly designed WC system may only become blocked through misuse. If there are children in the house, toys may find their way into the trap to form a barrier to other waste matter – a particular problem with double-trap siphonic WCs. Alternatively, the over-enthusiastic use of toilet paper can cause problems.

The first action is to isolate the cistern to prevent further flushing (use the service valve or tie up the float valve). Then the blockage can be tackled after donning protective rubber gloves, etc. A large plunger with a long handle may work, or a drain rod with rubber disc could be tried. On no account should rigid metal implements be used, as they will damage the WC bowl.

If these methods are ineffective, the plumber's 'snake' may be employed, although a larger size than that used on the sink will be necessary. However, even the snake will not be sufficiently flexible to pass around the double bends of a siphonic pan. An alternative approach may be via the soil stack, if a suitable access point is available, but care must be taken when removing the cover, in case the stack itself is blocked. In some cases, a blocked siphonic WC pan may have to be removed completely before an obstruction can be cleared.

Drains

The first indication of a blockage in the drain system will normally be the smell. Then gullies or inspection chambers will begin to overflow, or a downstairs WC or shower outlet may refuse to drain. Worse could be a back-up of effluent into a ground-floor shower tray.

The first action must be to turn off all appliances (including dishwashers, washing machines, etc), then the water system, to prevent further damage or back-up into the property. After that, two options are available: either call the nearest drainage contractor, or attempt to clear the blockage yourself. It is not a pleasant job, but is usually within the capabilities of a competent householder.

First, the blockage must be located, which can be done by lifting inspection chamber covers outside. Follow the line of the drains, lifting covers until you find a chamber that is not full; the blockage will be between this and the last full chamber.

If the drains pass through, and serve, neighbours' premises, check with them that they haven't got the same problem, and ask if you may check their inspection chambers to identify the position of the blockage. If the neighbours have a similar problem, something could be wrong with the main sewer. In this case, the local sewage authority should be called immediately so that remedial action may be taken as a matter of urgency.

If you have reason to believe that the blockage is due to root damage or the collapse of the drain, however caused, it would be prudent to employ a specialist contractor to carry out the repair.

Once the location of the blockage has been established, a drain set will be needed. This can be hired. The set will comprise a number of rods that can be screwed together, with a selection of accessories for fitting on the end. These may include a plunger, worm screw and scraper, each of which has a role to play in pushing, pulling or scraping debris out of the drain and into the nearest inspection chamber for removal. If the drain set is not effective, a large 'snake' may have to be hired, or a drainage contractor employed.

▶ SEE PAGE 152 FOR STEP-BY-STEP INSTRUCTIONS ON UNBLOCKING UNDERGROUND DRAINS

Re-washering a tap

With the notable exception of the Supatap, the water must be turned off and the cistern drained when replacing a washer, unless servicing valves have been fitted. If servicing valves have not been fitted, take the opportunity to fit them to the water supply pipes so that any future work on the tap, or its replacement, can be carried out without having to drain down the whole system again.

With the Supatap, simply unscrew the nut on the top of the tap body, and turn the tap on fully. When the tap is fully open, the head will come off, and the water will stop flowing.

Tap the nozzle on a hard surface to loosen the anti-splash device, and use a screwdriver to separate the washer/jumper unit from it. Replace the washer unit and re-assemble the tap in the reverse order.

With other types of spindle tap, the main head gear must be removed from the body of the tap by turning the large nut while holding the tap still with a second spanner or wrench. The washer (and jumper if not fixed) may then be removed, and the washer taken off after removing any securing nut. Re-assembly is a matter of reversing the sequence after fitting a new washer.

However, if the tap seat is damaged, a new washer will not stop a leak. Two methods can be used to rectify this. The seat can be re-cut with a tap reseating tool (hire it), which screws into the body and is turned to grind a new seat. Alternatively, a nylon insert can be fitted onto the old seat to seal against the new washer.

TOOLS AND MATERIALS

☐ Screwdriver
☐ Adjustable spanners
☐ Tap reseating tool (possibly)
☐ Tap washer
☐ Tap seat insert (possibly)

1 On a kitchen mixer of this type, turn the spout to the side and feel for the key moving into the unlocked position as you do so. When it is in the correct position, lift the spout up and remove it from the main body of the tap.

2 With the spout removed from the tap, the keyway that allows removal of the spout is revealed, as is the seating for the top rubber sealing washer. The O-ring has remained in the bottom of the tap body.

3 The small locking stud, which slots into the keyway, can be seen on the base of the spout. The top sealing washer has been removed, while the groove that accepts the O-ring seal can be seen at the very bottom.

4 The head gear for each side of the tap can be reached by simply pulling off the appropriate shroud handle. A splined plastic top to the tap body snaps into the handle and operates the tap spindle.

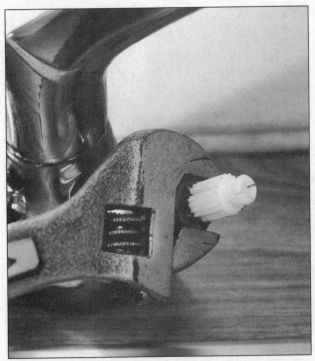

5 with the handle out of the way, you can unscrew the head gear from the body of the tap with an adjustable spanner. Take care when first slackening the head gear not to use too much force, as the spanner may slip and damage the sink.

6 To re-washer the tap, simply pull off the old washer and push on a new one. Then re-assemble the tap in the reverse order of dismantling. Finally, reinstate the water supply, and when it is running freely, close the tap.

Replacing a ceramic disc cartridge

Many modern taps do not use conventional spindles and washers, but instead employ a ceramic disk cartridge. This normally rotates through a quarter-turn from the closed position to fully open.

It is rare for a ceramic disc cartridge to fail. However, if one does fail, a complete replacement cartridge must be fitted. This must not only be of the correct size, but also of the correct 'hand' to ensure that the handle turns in the correct direction from off to on. These cartridges are much more expensive than old-fashioned washers, and there are several types to choose from. Therefore, it is essential to know the make and model of tap that is installed before purchasing a replacement, and professional help may be necessary to make the identification. Ideally, remove the defective cartridge and take it with you to a reputable plumbers' merchant, making sure that the water to the tap cannot accidentally be turned on in your absence.

Replacement is relatively easy. After the tap has been isolated from the water supply, the cover is removed to expose the screw holding the tap head. Removing this screw allows the head itself to be pulled off. Then the cartridge may be unscrewed with a spanner. The new cartridge is simply screwed in place, and the tap re-assembled.

TOOLS AND MATERIALS
☐ Screwdrivers
☐ Adjustable spanner
☐ Ceramic disc cartridge

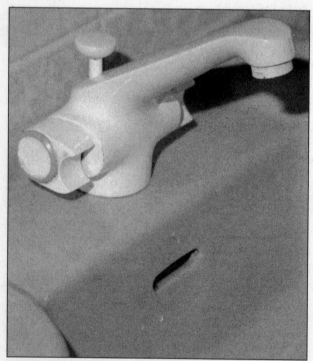

1 This monobloc basin mixer with pop-up waste is fitted with quarter-turn ceramic disc cartridges instead of conventional washers. The cartridges are 'handed' to allow operation in the correct direction depending on where they are fitted.

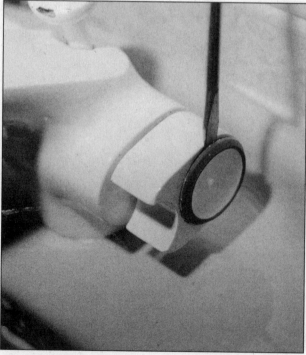

2 After shutting off the water to the appropriate side of the tap and letting the pipe drain, remove the colour-coded insert from the tap top, using a thin screwdriver. Take great care not to damage the handle of the tap or the insert itself.

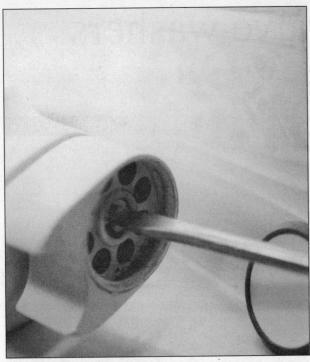

3 With the insert removed from the end of the handle, the handle fixing screw will be revealed. Slacken the screw to free the handle. Some handles will be held in place by a large metal disc as well as the screw.

4 Pull the handle off the splined shaft to reveal the top of the cartridge. In some cases, the handle may be fitted to a splined plastic insert which, in turn, is pushed onto the end of the cartridge spindle.

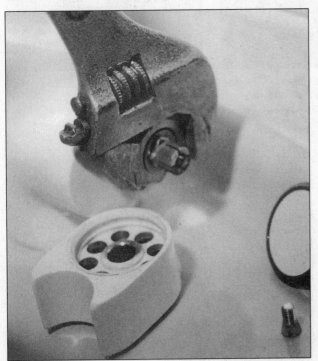

5 Use an adjustable spanner to unscrew the ceramic disc cartridge from the body of the tap. Take care not to slip with the spanner, as its handle may damage adjacent tiling or the top of the washbasin.

6 Make sure that the new cartridge is correctly 'handed' and screw it into the tap body. Re-assemble the components of the handle in the reverse order of dismantling. Reinstate the water supply, and when it is running freely, close the tap.

Replacing float valve washers

Persistent dripping or running from the overflow warning pipe of a cistern – whether it be a cold water storage cistern in the loft, or a WC cistern – usually means that the rubber washer in the float (ball) valve has perished, or that the float arm has not been set correctly. The latter situation is easy to remedy: a brass arm may be bent downwards so that the float is lower in relation to the valve, closing it at a lower water level; a plastic arm may be adjusted by slackening the locknut of its threaded stop, screwing the stop inwards, and locking it with the nut.

If the float is correctly positioned, the valve washer is most likely at fault. These two step-by step sequences show how to replace the washer of a modern plastic float valve, and also of a brass-bodied Portsmouth valve, which was

Modern plastic valve

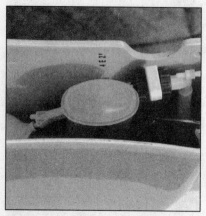

In a modern cistern, most of the components of the float valve and flushing mechanism are made from plastic, which does not suffer from corrosion.

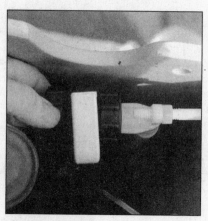

1 If the washer needs replacing, unscrew the nut that holds the float arm onto the valve body. You should not need any tools to do this.

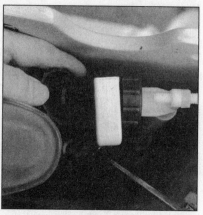

2 Carefully ease off the nut. As you do so, the washer will be exposed. Be prepared to catch it to prevent it from falling into the cistern.

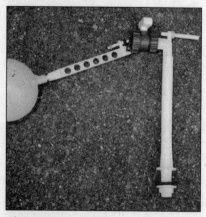

The complete valve assembly, showing the water inlet at the bottom. An adjuster is provided to alter the travel of the arm and set the water level.

3 The washer used in a plastic float valve will be much larger than the washer fitted to a brass Portsmouth valve. Make sure you have the correct type.

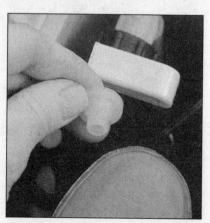

4 The washer closes against this internal nozzle. Two sizes are available, one for high-pressure systems, and a larger version for low-pressure systems.

commonly used before the introduction of plastic valves. In both cases, the water supply to the cistern must be isolated by turning off the servicing valve adjacent to the cistern, by turning off the valve on the supply pipe from the loft cistern, or by turning off the main stopvalve. If there is no servicing valve on the pipe to the cistern, take the opportunity to fit one at the same time as repairing the float valve. There is no need to drain the cistern itself while you carry out this job, but take care not to drop any small items into the water, as retrieving them may be difficult, particularly when working on the valve of a large storage cistern.

The plastic type of valve is unlikely to require any tools to replace the washer – it should be possible to unscrew the retaining nut by hand. However, the brass Portsmouth valve will probably have suffered from a degree of corrosion, and it may be necessary to use pliers or adjustable grips to remove the end of the valve body to gain access to the piston assembly.

TOOLS AND MATERIALS

☐ Pliers
☐ Screwdriver
☐ Valve washer

Brass Portsmouth valve

Prior to the widespread introduction of plastic valves, the brass-bodied Portsmouth valve was commonly fitted to both storage and WC cisterns.

1 For clarity, the valve is shown removed from the cistern, but this is not necessary. Unscrew the nut on the end, using grips if necessary.

2 Take out the split pin that secures the float arm. Then remove the arm, and push the piston assembly out of the valve body with a screwdriver.

3 Unscrew the cap to remove the washer. You may need to use pliers, preventing the piston from turning by inserting a screwdriver in its slot.

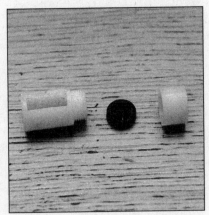

4 Simply push the old washer out of the cap, and replace it with a new one. Then screw the cap back onto the main body of the piston.

5 If necessary, the inlet nozzle can be reached by unscrewing the inlet body from the valve. Re-assemble the valve in the reverse order of dismantling.

Fitting a siphon flap valve

If a WC cistern is not flushing correctly, requiring the handle to be operated several times to start the water flowing, it is likely that the flap valve in the syphon has become damaged. The solution is to replace the flap which, though a straightforward job, will require the cistern to be partially dismantled.

To replace the flap valve, the entire siphon assembly must be removed from the cistern. First, turn off the water supply, flush the cistern, then mop out the water remaining in the bottom. Disconnect the siphon piston shaft from the operating lever, remove the flush pipe, and unscrew the plastic backnut holding the siphon assembly to the base of the cistern.

In the case of a close-coupled WC, after draining the cistern, the screws that hold it to the wall must be removed. Then, release the nuts holding the cistern to the back of the pan and lift the cistern free. Finally, unscrew the plastic nut holding the syphon in place, and lift this out of the cistern.

You may find that a new flap valve needs trimming to size, to match the old flap. Do this carefully, using the old flap as a pattern. After fitting the new flap valve, check that it moves freely inside the siphon unit.

TOOLS AND MATERIALS

- ☐ Screwdriver (possibly)
- ☐ Adjustable spanner (possibly)
- ☐ Scissors (possibly)
- ☐ Flap valve

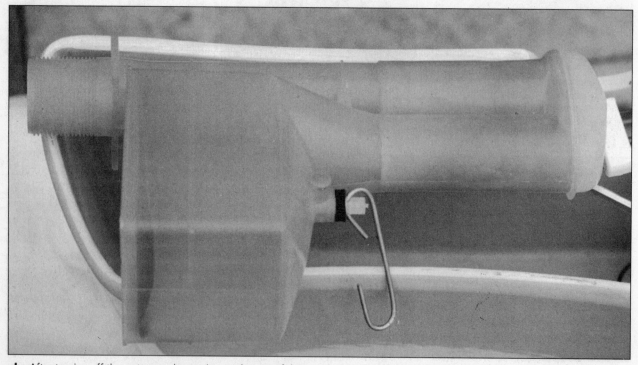

1 After turning off the water supply, or tying up the arm of the float valve, and emptying the cistern, the syphon assembly can be removed. To do this, it will be necessary to release the backnut holding it to the base of the cistern.

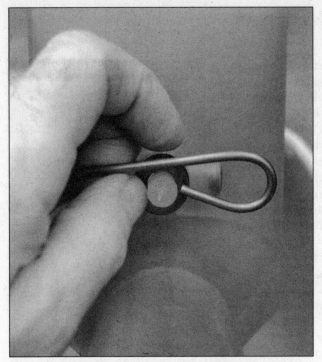

2 Unhook the metal link that connects the siphon assembly's piston rod to the operating lever. It may also be necessary to lift off a sealing washer. Then pull the piston assembly from the base of the siphon unit.

3 With the piston assembly removed, you will be able to see the flap valve and check its condition. If it is torn or damaged in any way, it will not perform correctly and should be replaced with a new flap.

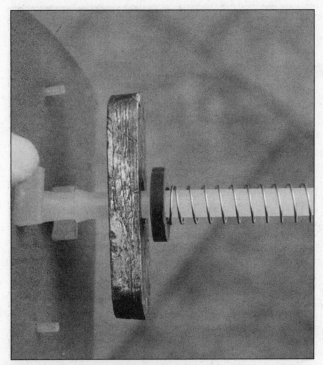

4 Remove the spring and and washer from the piston shaft. Then remove the flap retainer by prising it from its lugs. Finally, remove the old flap valve, lifting it from its locating pins on the piston unit.

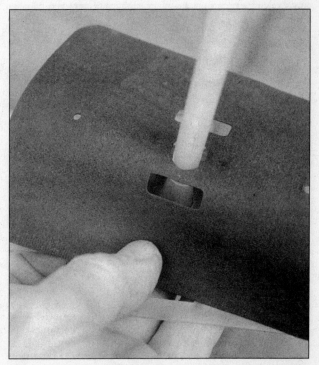

5 Replace the flap valve, slipping it over the lugs and pins of the piston unit. On older cisterns, the membrane will be of thick polythene, so extra care must be taken. Then re-assemble the siphon and cistern in the reverse order of dismantling.

Unblocking drains

When faced with a blocked drain, the first job is to find the exact location of the blockage. To start, lift the cover of the inspection chamber serving the property. If the inspection chamber is full, the blockage is downstream, so proceed along the line of chambers until one is found that is empty. The blockage will be between the empty chamber and the full one.

Using drain rods, most blockages can be approached from two sides: the clean side downstream or the full side, upstream. An approach from downstream will indicate the location of the blockage more clearly. If the blockage is in the interceptor trap of the upstream inspection chamber, the rods will find the retaining plug in the rodding arm and may, if it has not been cemented into position, push it out, releasing the backed-up effluent. Once the effluent has cleared, the trap can be thoroughly cleaned.

If the only option is to go in at the full chamber, search for the bottom channel with the plunger on the end of the rod, and follow this channel to the trap opening. Gently plunging the rod into the trap may force the obstruction out into the drain, where backed-up effluent will flush it away, at least into the next inspection trap, if not into the sewer.

When pushing or pulling drain rods through a drain, it may help to rotate the rods at the same time, but in a *clockwise* direction only. An anti-clockwise rotation could unscrew some types of rod, leaving a length in the drains as well as the original blockage. Good-quality rods have fittings that will not unscrew in this way.

1 Unless the cover of an inspection chamber has been lifted recently, the rim will probably be full of soil and rust, while the cover itself may have no handles. Rake out all the debris from around the rim, insert the edge of a spade or similar thin, but strong, metal implement under the cover, and lever down. When the cover lifts, push a stout balk of timber underneath to hold it open.

2 With one end of the cover supported by the wood, you will be able to see if the chamber is full or not. Once you have identified the chamber that needs attention, lift its cover away to one side. Take care when lifting the cover, bending your knees and keeping your back straight, as it is likely to be very heavy. If possible, get someone to help you. Alternatively, lift the raised end and 'walk' the cover away.

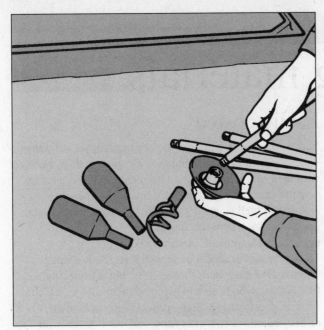

3 A set of drain rods will come with a number of different heads, some or all of which may be necessary to clear a blockage in a drain. It is probably best to select a simple plunger head first, as this may be all that is necessary to clear the blockage. Screw the head onto firmly onto the end of the first rod. If the plunger head appears to have no effect on the blockage, you can try one of the other heads.

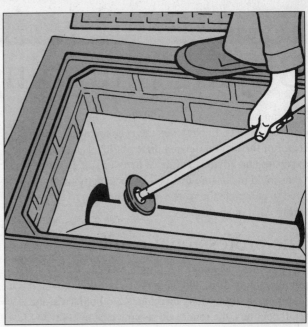

4 Attach a second rod onto the end of the first, making sure that they are firmly screwed together to prevent any likelihood of the rods parting company in the drain, which would be disastrous. Whether working from the upstream or downstream side of the blockage, lower the head of the rods into the channel at the bottom of the chamber and push the rods towards the blockage.

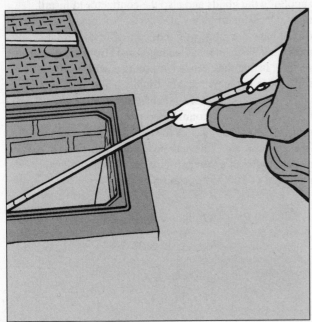

5 Push the rods into the drain, adding more rods as necessary until you reach the blockage. Then push and pull the rods firmly in and out to work the blockage free. It may also help to turn them in a clockwise direction. Don't be too vigorous when using drain rods, as over-enthusiasm can lead to damage, particularly with plastic drain pipes. This could result in a much more expensive repair.

6 After freeing the pipe, the interior of the inspection chamber should be washed down thoroughly with a hosepipe; a good flow of clean water will help to flush out any remaining sediment in the drain. Allow the water to run through the drain for a while. Then replace the cover. Gloves, protective clothing, the set of drain rods, and all other tools should be thoroughly cleaned and disinfected before being put away.

Buying plumbing materials

You can buy plumbing materials from a number of different outlets. Each serves the needs of a particular sector of the market, having different levels and areas of expertise and advice to offer. Wherever you go, however, you should make sure that you know exactly what you need to complete the work you are planning to carry out, and in what quantities.

The professional choice

The professional sources of plumbing materials are the plumbers' merchant and the builders' merchant who has a plumbing section. Many merchants run both trade and retail counters, the retail side serving customers who would otherwise use the DIY store.

Merchants stock the widest range of plumbing goods, tools, equipment and consumables, and are by far the best source for larger plumbing jobs. Many have showrooms displaying bathroom, kitchen and other wares, allowing their customers to see what is available and, most importantly, to discuss problems, ideas, etc.

They sell pipe in coils or long lengths, and fittings by the bag or box. Although merchants will supply items in small quantities, the price may not be very different to that found in a large DIY store. Consequently, the latter may be a more convenient source than buying the odd item from a plumbers' merchant.

A potential disadvantage with a merchant is that all the goods required for the job may not be on display, so you really must know what you want beforehand. Remember, too, that although most merchants have a great deal of knowledge about plumbing, they are there primarily to serve the trade - not to teach someone how to do the job.

Easily costed

Major DIY stores will offer a more limited, yet still fairly wide, range of products, and they are usually displayed with their individual prices. This means that it is easy to cost the materials required for a small job. These stores are usually well stocked with plastic waste and rainwater goods, but such items as copper pipe may only be available in lengths of 2m (6ft) maximum.

Like the merchants, the large DIY stores do display ranges of sanitaryware, showers, etc, but it is unusual to find anyone who is able to give technical advice, which is a major disadvantage. Some provide information on display boards or in leaflet form, but this is usually far from comprehensive.

Other sources

A third source of plumbing materials is a kitchen or bathroom centre or specialist, although generally these are geared almost exclusively to providing a design service, supplying the goods and also the contractor to install them. Occasionally, they also act as 'mini merchants', but do not have the range of goods carried by a normal merchant. Their main advantage, apart from the design service, is that their ranges of products will be different from those in the merchants, usually being more upmarket and exclusive - but more expensive.

Finally, the local ironmonger will probably offer a good range of tools, and may even stock a limited range of fittings, pipe, etc. This may be handy for the odd item needed to finish a job (particularly, if the plumbers' merchant or DIY store is miles away).

Finding a plumber

No matter how competent you are at carrying out plumbing work, there may be occasions when you need to employ a professional plumber. The problem then is how to find a good, reliable plumbing contractor. In any event, it is always a good idea to have the name of a good plumber to hand in case of an emergency that you are unable to deal with yourself.

Personal recommendation

By far the best way of finding a plumber that you can rely on is by word of mouth. Ask your friends and neighbours for their suggestions and recommendations, and for what jobs, as different plumbers specialise in different areas of plumbing work.

Professional bodies

Another way of finding a good plumber is to turn to the classified telephone directories. Here, you should look for a plumber who is a member of the Institute of Plumbing (IOP), or who is a Registered Plumber. Members should abide by the Institute's Code of Practice to carry out satisfactory work at a reasonable price. Another qualifying association is the National Association of Plumbing, Heating and Mechanical Services Contractors (NAPH & MSC), which also operates a code of practice. In fact, it is the only code of practice in the industry to be approved by the Office of Fair Trading. This association also offers an indemnity against the failure of the contractor to finish the job in a satisfactory manner. Another organisation of professionals is the Heating and Ventilating Contractors Association. Again, this organisation also has its own code of practice.

The only other organisation to offer reasonable guarantees to the consumer, for the work carried out by its members, is the AA Homeline - a national emergency service recently set up by the Automobile Association for the benefit of its subscribers and covering all trades, not just plumbing. Contractors associated with this organisation are drawn from qualified operators who are members of the IOP or NAPH & MSC, or who can demonstrate clearly their competence and fair trading to the association.

Rates are checked and approved by the AA. At the time of writing, fees up to £250 are paid directly to the AA, and not the contractor. Beyond that figure, the householder is recommended to seek quotations from several sources, but the contractor is paid direct.

There are several other 'trade' associations in the UK, but the technical competence of their members, and the fairness of their trading methods is not monitored by professional associations noted above.

Note In respect of gas installations, the Council for the Registration of Gas Installers (CORGI) is concerned only with the technical competence of an installer, as it applies to gas installation, servicing and maintenance. It has no jurisdiction over any other aspect of plumbing or heating, nor of the fairness of the installer's trading practice.

Glossary

Anti-siphon valve A device fitted into pipework to prevent back-siphonage occurring.

Backnut Fitted to the threaded shank of a tap to clamp it into place.

Back-siphonage Can occur with flexible shower hoses and garden hosepipes if the end should be under water and the supply pressure drops. This leads to flow in the opposite direction, which can contaminate the water supply.

Balanced supply Hot and cold water supplies from the same form of source (the mains or storage) and, therefore, having the same pressure.

Ball valve A form of isolating valve containing a ball with a hole to control flow. Also used to describe a float valve with a ball-shaped float.

Bar A unit of pressure applied to water supplies.

Benching The sloping cement mortar surface that borders the channels at the bottom of an inspection chamber.

Bib tap A tap that can be screwed into a wall plate.

Capillary joint A soldered pipe joint of any kind.

Capnut Used on a compression fitting to clamp against the olive and ensure a watertight seal.

Ceramic disc cartridge Used in some taps in place of a conventional washer. Water flow is controlled by two ceramic discs with cutouts, the range of movement from closed to fully open being a quarter-turn.

Cesspool Installed where connection to the main sewer is not possible. Collects soil from WCs and must be emptied regularly.

Cistern A cold water storage tank.

Combi boiler A form of instantaneous water heater with a central heating function.

Compression joint A mechanical pipe joint that makes a watertight seal by compressing a special metal ring (an olive) between the pipe and body of the joint.

Crowsfoot spanner A specially-shaped tool that can reach behind basins, sinks and baths to tighten or unscrew the tap nuts.

Direct system In a direct cold water system, all of the cold outlets in the are supplied direct from the mains; in a direct hot system, all water passes through the boiler's heat exchanger.

'Domex' screw A screw with a special dome-shaped cover that conceals its head.

Double check valve A device fitted into pipework to prevent back-siphonage occurring.

Earth bonding A method of linking all the metal components of a plumbing system to prevent them from becoming electrically 'live'.

Elbow A pipe joint for changing the direction of a run, either through 90 degrees or 135 degrees.

End-feed joint A capillary joint in which molten solder is fed into the end to make a watertight seal.

Expansion vessel Used in unvented hot water systems to accommodate the expansion of hot water.

Fall The gradient of a waste pipe or guttering to ensure that water runs away efficiently.

Feed and expansion pipe The draw-off pipe from a hot water cylinder that continues up to the cold water storage cistern, where it can discharge overheated water.

Feed and expansion tank A small cistern for topping up a central heating system and providing a receptacle for overheated water.

Float valve Controls water flow into a cistern, and operated by a float in the cistern.

Flux A chemical metal cleaner used in conjunction with solder.

Gate valve Controls water flow by means of a flap that closes off the bore of the valve.

Gland nut Tightens against the gland packing of a tap to ensure a watertight seal.

Gland packing A waterproof material used to seal around the spindle of a tap.

Gully A trapped outdoor connection to the underground drains. A grid prevents leaves and other debris from falling into the gully, while pipes may either pass through the grid to discharge into the system, or be attached to special sockets.

Head Refers to the height between the bottom of a storage cistern and the water outlet (a tap or shower head, for example). The greater the head, the greater the water pressure at the outlet.

Hopper head An open funnel-shaped collector used in a two-pipe waste system to collect water from basin, bath and shower waste pipes.

HSS High-speed steel; refers to a type of drill bit suitable for drilling metal components.

Indirect system In an indirect cold water system, all outlets (with the exception of the kitchen cold tap) are supplied with water from a storage cistern; in an indirect hot system, water supplied to the outlets is separated from water that passes through the boiler. The latter passes through a coil heat exchanger in the hot water cylinder.

Inspection chamber Allows access to the underground drains.

Jumper Carries the washer in a conventional tap.

'Kupla' fitting A special bracket for connecting a basin to its pedestal.

Manifold Fitted to the end of a section of concealed pipework to provide multiple outlets.

Microbore pipe Narrow copper pipe up to 12mm diameter.

Mixer tap A tap that can deliver both hot and cold water through a single spout.

Monobloc mixer A mixer tap that requires a single mounting hole.

Multipoint heater An electric or gas-fired water heater that can service several outlets.

Multikwik extension A simple push-on connector for joining a WC outlet to the soil pipe.

Munzing ring A form of pipe clip that holds the pipe clear of the adjacent surface.

Olive A soft metal ring used in a compression joint and clamped between the joint and pipe to provide a watertight seal.

O-ring A soft rubber ring used to provide a watertight seal in push-fit pipe fittings and some forms of tap.

Pillar tap An individual tap for supplying either hot or cold water. A wide range of styles is available.

Pipe-in-pipe system A system of running pipes through pipes of larger diameter, either to protect them or to allow them to be removed from walls, etc, with little disturbance to the surroundings.

Potable Means that water is fit for human consumption and refers to the quality of water supplied by the local water authority.

Primary circuit The heating circuit from a boiler to the hot water cylinder in an indirect hot system. The water in the primary circuit never mixes with water that is delivered to the hot taps.

Push-fit joint A method of joining pipes that requires no mechanical tightening or sealing of any kind. The fitting is simply pushed onto the end of the pipe, rubber O-rings providing a watertight seal.

Rising main The pipe that carries water up into the house from the underground supply. Normally, it rises in the kitchen, or close to it.

Rodding eye An access point on the underground drainage system that allows insertion of drain rods for clearing blockages.

Self-cutting connector Often supplied with washing machine and outdoor tap plumbing kits. The connector, which may also incorporate an ON/OFF valve, is simply attached to a convenient supply pipe, and as it is tightened it cuts into the pipe, making the connection. Usually, there is no need to turn off the water supply.

Septic tank Installed where connection to the underground sewer is not possible. It collects soil from the WCs, treating some of it so that it may be discharged into the ground. Sediment must be regularly emptied from the tank

Service pipe The underground pipe that carries water from the water authority's stopvalve to the rising main. The service pipe is the householder's responsibility.

Servicing valve A form of isolating valve that allows the water supply to a particular outlet to be shut off.

Single point-of-use heater An electric or gas-fired water heater that services one outlet only.

Single-stack system A waste system in which all soil and waste outlets are connected to a single vertical pipe that, in turn, is connected to the underground drain.

Siphon flap valve Fitted to a WC flushing mechanism to control the flow of water from the cistern into the pan.

Smallbore pipe 15mm copper pipe.

Soil stack The vertical pipe of a single-stack waste system. It may be attached to an outside wall or, in a modern building, run down inside.

Solder A soft metal supplied in stick or wire form for making capillary joints. When touched onto the pre-heated joint, the solder melts and flows into the joint to seal it.

Solder-ring joint A pipe fitting that contains a ring of solder. To make the joint, all that is necessary is to heat the fitting until the solder melts.

Solvent-weld joint Used with some forms of plastic pipe. The solvent effectively 'welds' the pipe and fitting together.

Standpipe Used with a trap for a washing machine or dishwasher; the waste hose from the machine simply hooks into the top of the pipe.

Stopcock, Stoptap, Stopvalve A form of isolating valve that controls water flow like a tap, forcing a flexible washer down onto the water inlet inside the body of the valve.

Strap boss A connector that can be fitted to a soil stack to allow connection of a waste pipe.

Tee A fitting that allows connection of a branch pipe to a supply pipe.

Throating A narrowing of the bore of a copper pipe when it has been bent incorrectly.

'Top hat' washer Fitted to the shank of a tap to allow for any unthreaded portion.

Trap Fitted to all waste outlets and containing a water seal to prevent drain smells from reaching the interior of the house.

Two-pipe system Old form of waste system in which soil from WCs is taken to a soil stack, while waste water from basins, baths, etc, is discharged into hopper at the top of a second pipe, or into a gully.

Unbalanced supply Hot and cold water from separate sources (one from storage, one from the mains), leading to a pressure differential.

Unvented system A hot water system in which expansion is accommodated by an expansion vessel rather than an expansion pipe.

Vent pipe See below.

Vented system Hot water system in which a vent pipe is provided to accommodate expansion of the hot water. The vent pipe terminates over the cold water storage cistern so that in severe cases, expanding hot water can be discharged into it.

Warning pipe Also known as overflow pipe. Normally, it discharges to the outside; water flowing from the pipe indicates that the level in a cistern is too high.

Wiped joint A form of soldered joint used with lead pipe.

Index

Acknowledgements

Written by   Derek Johnson

Editor   Ian Penberthy

Designed   David Hermelin
                  Rhian Walters

Indexed   Rachel Rogers

The author and publishers would like to thank
the following companies for their participation
and support in providing technical advice,
illustrations and photographs.

Doulton Bathroom Products
Albion, The Cylinder People
Aqua-Dial
Aqualisa Products
Armitage Shanks
Armstrong World Industries
Bristan
Caradon Mira

Daryl Industries
Ecowater Systems
Flamco Brefco
Franke (UK)
John Guest
The Haigh Tweeny Co
Heatrae Sadia Heating
Hepworth Building Products
Hunter Building Products
IBP Conex
IMI Waterheating
Ideal Standard
Leisure
Marley Extrusions
Monument Tools
Opella
Pegler
Saniflo
Showerlux (UK)
T & D Industries
Triton